Old Master
Prints and Drawings

2. Ugo da Carpi *Diogenes*   chiaroscuro woodcut, circa 1527

R. Stanley Johnson

OLD MASTER

PRINTS AND DRAWINGS

*

A Critical Essay

THOUGHTS ON COLLECTING

PRINTS AND DRAWINGS

*

Spring 2005

R. S. JOHNSON FINE ART
645 N. Michigan Ave., Chicago, IL 60611
(312) 943-1661 Fax (312) 943-1642
www.rsjohnsonfineart.com

Publication No. 147
*

Research, Consultation and Advice
Ursula M. Johnson
*

Special Assistance
Suzanne Smycz
Jacob Fish
*

ISBN No. 0-9728927-3-7
Library of Congress Catalogue Card No. 2005900321
All Rights Reserved
No parts of the contents of this publication
may be reproduced without written
consent from its authors
Published Spring 2005
*

Distributed by
Klees/Gustorf Publishers
Chicago/Düsseldorf

*

Est. in 1955 by S. E. Johnson (1904-1967)

On Cover
36. JAN HARMENSZ. MULLER (1571 - 1628)
Bellona Leading the Armies of the Emperor Against the Turks (1st State), 1600
Engraving after Bartholomeus Spranger (1546 - 1611)
(detail)

A Critical Essay
THOUGHTS ON COLLECTING
PRINTS AND DRAWINGS

From fifteenth and sixteenth century chateaux, palazzi and villas to twenty-first century country estates, townhouses and lofts, there has always been a vast number of walls in need of decoration. This need sometimes is satisfied with inherited paintings, tapestries. heraldic armory or hunting trophies and at other times with newly acquired or commissioned works by artists from the past or the present. Once their palazzi and townhouses have been decorated, however, there remain those who still wish to continue acquiring works of art. One possible fulfillment of this desire could be through the acquisition of more palazzi or townhouses, encouraging the acquisition of still more paintings and other decoration to cover the added walls. Another solution could be to turn to collecting artists' drawings, prints and other more intimately conceived works of art, not particularly useful as decoration, but capable of providing great pleasure for the collector. Such works take up limited wall-space and even can be stored in unobtrusive bins or boxes. At this point, we have in one form or another the possible origins of an eventual, passionate collector of prints and drawings.

Collecting prints and drawings is not a recent or isolated phenomenon in Western art. Such collections have been created for more than five centuries. One might cite the print collection of Ferdinand Columbus (1488-1539) in Spain, the drawing collections of Nicholas Lanier (1588-1666) in Stuart England and Pierre Crozat (1665-1740) in France, the Chatsworth collections of prints and drawings centering around William Cavendish, 2nd Duke of Devonshire (1673-1729), or the more recent collection of works on paper of the late New York collector, Ian Woodner (1903-1990).

The desire to acquire prints and drawings can manifest itself sooner, later or never in the lifetime of an art collector. One attraction of particularly old master but also of modern prints and drawings is that their usually small formats tend to make them more meaningful and enriching to the eye and the mind in that they are more easily comparable to other works by the same or different artists. Historical, biblical, mythological and other aspects and often the closeness of works on paper to the printed word makes them, beyond aesthetics, intellectually challenging and satisfying. Added pleasure is to be derived from the connoisseurship and detective-like research involving provenance, references, watermarks, condition, quality of impressions and finally an assessment of the originality and spontaneity of conception of each work. There also are different and changing viewpoints to be considered in evaluating prints and drawings. For example, in past centuries great importance was accorded to the choice of subject: recent emphasis is placed rather on the artist involved and that artist's ability as a printmaker or draughtsman, thus on the manner in which subjects are represented rather than on the things they represent. Collecting works on paper results in the discoveries of many differently layered techinical and cultural informations. The individual choices and resulting ensemble of such works becomes a fascinatingly accurate reflection of a collector's taste, sensitivity and sophistication. It is for these and many other reasons that, as their acquisition interests and philosophies evolve, the more reflective collectors of paintings and other decorative works, in case after case, turn towards works on paper.

The images created through prints and drawings, once printed or drawn on a piece of paper, usually cannot be changed. In the case of a painting, on the other hand, the artist has unlimited possibilities to make corrections and revisions. These latter changes depend primarily on the artist's own intentions and sensitivities, but also take into account his or her intuitions concerning the feelings and judgments of others, viewers who could be the artist's friends, critics, as well as a present and future general public. Each resulting redefinition of a painting, every painted addition or subtraction, is a step away from the level of spontaneity and that immediacy found more often in an artist's prints and drawings. This is not to say that "spontaneity" and "immediacy" are never

50. Rembrandt *The Descent from the Cross by Torchlight*, etching and drypoint, 1654

present in paintings: we have only to consider the superb oil sketches of Rubens to disprove that general statement. This is also not to reject the acquisition of paintings: virtually all significant collectors, including some with the greatest holdings of prints and drawings, have acquired fine paintings. It also does not mean that spontaneity and immediacy always are present in works on paper: many over-worked drawings and various types of laboriously-produced reproductive prints would disprove that general statement as well. What we are stating is that the spontaneity and the immediacy of an artistic presence, our comprehension of the intimate inner workings and possible genius of an artist and our true pleasure in his or her works are more likely attainable through our possession and contemplation of carefully chosen examples of that artist's original works on paper.

*   *   *

Every collector has personal ideas and ideals which influence collecting decisions. Changing predilections can concern anything from a preference of works on paper over paintings, an attraction to certain artists, subjects or colors, as well as possible adherence to wide-ranging art historical theories. There are always questions as to what extent these feelings and leanings should be sublimated to pre-established "standards" and to the "balance" of a given collection. In recognizing and weighing such inter-related facets and elements of a considered acquisition, a collector is more able to understand, along with the qualities of a given work of art, its capacity to enhance and enrich a particular collection.

A collector sometimes is subject to sudden and even passionate attractions towards specific works of art. This might result in casting aside a certain degree of logic and carefully established principles in order to take immediate advantage of an acquisition opportunity. Prior to making an intelligent acquisition, however, many objective facts first have to be considered: questions of authenticity, historical significance, relative quality within a given artist's works, condition, provenance, exhibition participation, pertinent references, expert opinions and others. As an example, each possible addition to a collection has to be judged as to the work's rareness, keeping in mind that the last available examples of a desired category logically take precedence over acquisitions from equally desired but less rare categories. Utilizing such logic, a collector could decide, for instance, to acquire an early impression of a woodcut by Albrecht Dürer rather than an impression printed later, or to acquire an outstanding drypoint by Rembrandt or a fine drawing by Picasso rather than a less rare, recent work by a more contemporary artist. Rareness also must be related to condition: the rarer an object, the more a collector has to be willing to accept certain problems of condition. Another question is to what extent a contemplated acquisition might build onto the strengths or weaknesses of an already established collection. As a collection develops, the desirability and even necessity of each new acquisition becomes increasingly pre-determined through a collector's perception of *lacunae* in the ensemble of works already acquired. An expanding collection thus has a life of its own and in time tends to determine from within itself the nature and choice of new acquisitions. In their acquisition decisions, the most impassioned and also independent-minded collectors gradually fall into the hands of their own collections.

*   *   *

For an over-view of thoughts on collecting, whatever the media involved, it is important to point out that there are fundamental differences between private collections and those of public institutions. Museums often strive to be encyclopedic, while private collections, though possibly very extensive in one area or another, are not necessarily so driven nor are they usually capable of achieving such lofty objectives. The holdings of a typical museum, a combination of private donations and curatorial decisions, ostensibly are formed for the edification of a general public. The development of those holdings depends to a certain extent on the competence and the possible idiosyncrasies of curators as well as those curators' capacity to stand above the changing tastes and fashions of the times. In addition, the public institution often is more or less obliged to accept just about any art donation, no matter of what quality or benefit for eventual public viewing. At the same time, the museum and its curators, in spending private or public funds for their acquisitions, exhibitions and costs of conservation, must court to one degree or another the approval of specific segments of that same general public. This fragmented public approval extends from the views of art critics to those of important donors, and finally to the judgments of elected or appointed officials, without whose support institutions often cannot exist. Private holdings, on the other hand, assembled for the pleasure of individuals, generally have no special, external obligations. Such collections ideally are not concerned with changing tastes and fashions, demand no public accountability and are freely and very personally conceived.

*   *   *

The legendary Dutch expert Frits Lugt once wrote that "a collector is a constructor". True enough! Once a building is completed, however, a construction ends. When even a modest collection is being built, there never is an end. There are always new and exciting additions to be made: carefully and with exacting connoisseurship, but always with passion.

R. Stanley Johnson
April, 2005

10. The Master FG, engraving after Primaticcio, circa 1530

INDEX OF ARTISTS

I
French and Italian
Prints and Drawings 1500-1700

1. NORTHERN FRENCH MASTER, about 1500

The Virgin and Child Enthroned, Northern France, perhaps Paris, about 1500

Large miniature on a leaf of an illuminated manuscript in French verse on vellum
214 x 150 mm.; 8 1/2 x 5 7/8 inches

Notes:
This work is from a *Book of Hours* or similar prayerbook. Here the Virgin is shown crowned and holding the Child as two angels hover at the sides, lifting the curtains of a canopy around the throne. Painted in colors and liquid gold, the miniature itself measures 70 x 90 mm. This scene is presented above a large initial and the verse in French (which is complete): "Glorieuse virge marie" (see: A. Langfors *Les Incipits des poèmes français*, 1917, p. 149). The verso is ruled for twenty-seven lines, with full-length panel border of colored flowers and acanthus leaves on partially-colored gold ground.

2. UGO DA CARPI
Carpi 1480-circa 1532 Rome

Diogenes, circa 1527

Chiaroscuro woodcut, four blocks, after Francesco Parmigianino (Parma 1503 -1540 Casal Maggiore)
490 x 354 mm.; 19 1/4 x 14 inches

References:
BartschXII.100.10
Jan Johnson"Ugo da Carpi's Chiaroscuro Woodcuts", *Print Collector,* nos. 57-58: 2-87,1982.
David Landau and Peter Parshall *The Renaissance Print,* Yale University Press, New Haven and London, 1994 (pp. 150-154).
Evelyn Lincoln *The Invention of the Italian Renaissance Printmaker,* Yale University Press, New Haven and London, 2000: pp. 75-85.

Notes:
1. A very fine impression, printing with excellent and subtle color register.
2. In considering Ugo da Carpi as a printmaker, Landau and Parshall (referring often to Jan Johnson's research - see texts cited above) note that Ugo had moved to Rome where he set up shop by 1518. It was then that Ugo finished the woodcut *Death of Ananias* which Ugo's inscription calls "after Raphael". Actually, Ugo's woodcut appears to be rather after an engraving "after Raphael" of the same subject by Agostino Veneziano (B. XIV.48.43). Landau and Parshall conclude (p. 150, ref. cited above) that the *Death of Ananias,* together with a number of other Ugo da Carpi woodcuts, comes closest to a truly "reproductive print". Landau and Parshall go on to note, however, that such a "reproductive" print does not "reproduce" a completed painting or drawing but is the copy of another print. One conclusion is that "Ugo had no obligation towards Raphael...or any other printmaker, and he was printing...on his own premises". It was thus that Ugo felt "free not only to copy Agostino Veneziano's or Marcantonio's prints...but also to inscribe them with Raphael's name..." Another conclusion of Landau and Parshall (pp. 150 and 153) is that it is "unlikely that Ugo produced many prints that were not copies of other prints" rather than "original, independent works made alone or in collaboration with another artist". In any case, Ugo had been raised in "the block-cutters's tradition" and always described himself as "a cutter or a printer". It is this fact above all which determined the true nature of his printmaking activities.

(text continues on page 12)

ioneule uirge marie.
A toy me rens et si te prie.
Que tu me veilles aider.
En ce que ie mestier
Garde mon corps de villennie.
Et tien mon cueur en ta baillie.
Et me fais tousiours uiure en paix.
Et me garde des maulx meffaix.
Qui ne me puisse chose faire.
Qui a ihesus puisse desplaire.
Et si te prie uierge honoree.
Que ie puisse passer la iournee.
Sans pechiez mortellement.
Et sans mourir villainnement.
Et me doint repentence telle.

3. The subject of this spectacular *chiaroscuro* (the realization of an image in terms of light and shadow rather than line) woodcut is the cynic-philosopher Diogenes (c. 412-312 B.C.) who incessantly wandered about Greece "with a lamp in broad daylight - vainly looking for an honest man". In referring to this work, Landau and Parshall (p. 154) describe it as "what is universally considered Ugo da Carpi's masterpiece". It must be noted that this work is very close in concept to a Jacopo Caraglio engraving (B.XV.94.61). Nevertheless, it would not appear plausible that Ugo could have copied his masterpiece from Caraglio's presumably later, smaller and weaker treatment of this same subject. Landau and Parshall believe that in his *Diogenes*, Ugo "must have had Parmigianino's hand [perhaps in the form of a drawing] very close to his woodblock when he produced it".

(illustrated on page 2)

3. CHRISTOFANO ROBETTA
Florence 1462-1552 or earlier, in Florence

Adoration of the Magi, about 1496-1500

Engraving
302 x 281 mm.; 11 7/8 x 11 1/16 inches

Watermark:
Hind watermark 71, which refers to Briquet watermark 8390 where dated 1529

Reference:
Hind I, page 200, no. D.II.10
Early Italian Engravings, National Gallery of Art, Washington D.C., 1973: no. 118, repr. p. 297

Notes:
1. A brilliant, early impression of this major work. With fully visible plate-lines on all four sides and additional margin (7 to 10 mm.) on three sides. Early impressions of this engraving are extremely rare, while later impressions, such as the impression in the National Gallery of Art (*Early Italian Engravings*, National Gallery of Art, Washington D. C., 1973: no. 118) are more common.
2. This engraving appears to have been inspired by Filippino Lippi's *Adoration of the Magi* of 1496 at the Uffizi Museum in Florence. It also is closely related to Leonardo da Vinci's *Adoration of the Magi* also at the Uffizi. This latter unfinished work would appear to have been a commission dating 1481and from the monks of San Donato at Scopeto, a commission to have been terminated in less than thirty months. In 1482, da Vinci moved to Milan and left this painting in the home of Amerio Benci. Art historians have found this date of 1482 hard to believe, as the painting appears to be too far in advance of its times. E. Muntz, for example, could not accept any date before 1500. In any case, there should also be mentioned as possible inspirations for this engraving: Sandro Botticelli's *Adoration of the Magi*, at the Uffizi but dating from the 1470's, and Domenico Ghirlandaio's *Adoration* in Florence at the Spedale degli Innocenti. In its treatment of the indiviual figures, however, this engraving still seems closest to the Filippino Lippi painting. On the other hand, in its pyramidal composition, Robetta's work approaches closest the Leonardo da Vinci. Robetta's engraving, if not actually autonomous, also could have been based on a lesser known or lost study by one of the above mentioned artists or his circle.

4. ANDREA MANTEGNA (workshop)
Padua 1431-1506 Mantua

Adoration of the Magi, about 1475-80

Engraving with greenish-brown wash added
383 x 284 mm.; 15 x 11 1/8 inches

Watermark: *Cardinal's Hat* (similar to Briquet 3403, dated 1503)

Provanance:
Chatsworth Collection (Dukes of Devonshire)
The Chatsworth Settlement, Christies, London, Dec. 5, 1985: no. 50

Literature:
A. M. Hind, *Catalogue of Early Italian Engravings in the British Museum*, 1910, p. 350, no. 8
T. Borenius, *Four Early Italian Engravers,* 1923, p. 37
A. M. Hind, *Early Italian Engraving*, 1948, Part II, vol V, P. 22
Illustrated Bartsch , vol. 25, p. 99

Reference:
Bartsch XIII, 233, 9
Hind V, 13
Early Italian Engravers, National Gallery of Art, Washington, D. C., 1975: cat. no. 81.

Notes:
1. A superb, sharp and rich impression of this extraordinarily rare, unfinished engraving. Printed in brown ink, with considerable tone. With a *Cardinal's Hat* watermark similar to Briquet watermark 3403 which gives possible dates for an Italian-made paper of: Venice 1481 (most probable), 1492, 1493, 1494 and 1501 as well as Udine 1503. There are greenish-brown wash additions to Saint-Joseph and to one of the Magi. These additions appear to have been contemporary.
2. In the 1948 edition of Hind's *Early Italian Engravings*, sixteen known impressions of the work, including this Chatsworth impression, are recorded. In addition, not cited by Hind, there is a seventeenth impression at the Cleveland Museum. At this time, this Chatsworth impression is the only one of the above not in a museum collection. Though not indicated either in Hind or the Chatsworth catalogue, there appear to be, among these seventeen impressions, two states of this engraving. This Chatsworth impression would appear to be clearly a 1st State before various additions, including a series of lines in the lower center of the image. The 2nd State impressions, such as the one at the Art Institute of Chicago, show considerable wear and appear to be later sixteenth century impressions lacking the finer and sharper qualities of the earlier impresssions.
3. This engraving is quite close in subject matter to the lower-right section of Mantegna's *Adoration of the Magi,* the center-panel of the triptych in the Uffizi Museum in Florence. The triptych generally is dated 1460-1466. However, Jacquelyn L. Sheehan, in her description of the Rosenwald impression in the National Gallery of Art (no. 81 of: *Early Italian Engravings*, National Gallery of Art, Washington D. C., 1973) points out that the forceful technique in this engraving as well as the repeated use of zig-zag strokes in the manner of Pollaiuolo all "makes it clear that the print was not executed before 1475, when Mantegna himself seems to have begun working in this manner." Sheehan goes on to note that this particular engraving is very different from the style of Zoan Andrea, who was working after the works of Mantegna at this same time. In addition... "the richness of the technique, the strong feeling for plasticity, and the fine differentiation of strength in the contour lines, particularly evident in the unfinished

(text continues on page 16)

portions of the engraving"... distinguish this work from the weaker works of Giovanni Antonio da Brescia and other Mantegna copyists of this period. There thus is the possibility that this work should be included in the small group of engravings attributed to Mantegna himself. However, it does appear difficult to believe, in view of the years of apprenticeship necessary to produce the quality level of the engravings now assigned to Mantegna himself, that the artist would have executed only seven or eight engravings as Hind and others have indicated. In conclusion, barring more conclusive evidence than that found in Hind's catalogue that would prove that Mantegna himself did any engravings at all, it would appear difficult to continue to agree with the clear division indicated by Hind of "Mantegna" and "School of Mantegna" engravings. Until further evidence appears to the contrary, we place all of these "Mantegna" and "School of Mantegna" engravings under aspects of the general heading of "School of Mantegna".

4. A young archivist, Andrea Canova, doing research on the Gonzaga Family of Mantova, has discovered a contract of 1475 between Andrea Mantegna and an engraver named Gian Marco Cavalli. In this notarized contract, Andrea Mantegna requests Gian Marco Cavalli to produce engravings after a certain number of Mantegna's drawings.This is a further indication that the works, until recently catalogued as "Mantegna engravings", were not executed by Mantegna himself but rather by one of his assistants. This discovery of Canova was published in an article: "*Bella Scoperta : Mantegna disegnava ma non incideva*" (A Great Discovery : Mantegna Drew But Did Not Engrave) which appeared in the *ARTE* section of *IL SOLE-24 ORE/5/*III, 2000.

Collection: Private Collection

5. MARCO DENTE
Ravenna about 1493 - 1527 Rome

Venus Seeks Advice from Juno and Ceres, circa 1518-1519

Engraving after Raphael Sanzio (Urbino 1483 - 1520 Rome)
260 x 201 mm.; 10 1/4 x 7 15/16 inches

Watermark: *Anchor in Circle*

Provenance: With the duplicate mark of the Kunsthalle Bremen.

Reference: Bartsch XIV, 247, 327.

Notes:
1. A very fine, sharp and, in its quality, extrremely rare impression of one of the graphic masterpieces of Marco Dente. This work was based on a drawing by Raphael now in the Albertina in Vienna.
2. In 1510, Marco Dente went from his native Ravenna to Rome where he became a student of Marcantonio Raimondi whose engraving technique he followed quite closely. Dente's productive life was rather limited since he died at the age of thirty-four in the Sack of Rome in 1527.
3. Marco Dente is one of a trio of artists, the others being Marcantonio Raimondi (1480 - 1527/34) and Agostino Veneziano (b. 1490), who executed some of the most beautiful engravings after Raphael. Most of these works were sold by the dealer Il Baviera. After the death of Raphael in 1520, Il Baviera apparently held onto the plates and, from that point on, took all the profit for himself -to the detriment of the interests of the printmakers themselves. Landau and Parshall (*The Renaissance Print*, 1994: p. 146) have suggested that, with few exceptions, both personal forgeries [copies of their own previously executed plates by Dente, Marcantonio and Veneziano] and any of the prints signed with the monogram or with a tablet -empty or not-, produced after 1520, were meant to damage Il Baviera and "to redress the financial balance of the whole operation in favor of the engravers".

6. ANDREA MANTEGNA (workshop)
Padua 1431-1506 Mantua

Bacchanal with a Wine Vat

Pen and black ink with wash, laid down on a contemporary sheet. Various voids, repairs. Considering its age, this sheet is in good condition.
290 x 354 mm.; 11 1/2 x 14 inches

Notes:
This major drawing is related to the Mantegna-executed or inspired engraving *Bacchanal with a Wine Vat*, one of the more important graphic works produced in northern Italy in the last half of the fifteenth century. The manner and quality of the drawing, the nature of the paper as well as the type and color of the brown-red ink employed all apperar to confirm the placing of this drawing within the circle of Andrea Mantegna.

Like some other working drawings related to Mantegna-studio engravings, this drawing represents only a part of the image of the final engraving. The vertical dimensions of the drawing and the engraving are close (299 vs 290 mm.). Among elements found in the final engraving, but not included in the present composition, are the laden vine rising behind the vat and the post to which it is secured behind the central satyr. While all ten figures on the left and center of the drawing are treated similarly to the same ten figures in the engraving, there are many differences between this drawing and the engraving. For example, the water jug in the engraving is more elongated than in the drawing. The head of the left putto is differently placed in relation to the lines on the vat. The spacial relations of the feet of all the figures are different than the engraving. Also, the precisely hatched lines found in the engraving are not in the drawing. These and other differences lead us to conclude that this drawing was not executed *after* the engraving but is either a preparatory *disegno* for the engraving or a working-drawing *after* a lost preparatory study for the engraving.

This drawing can be compared with a number of drawings reproduced in the recent exhibition catallogue *Andrea Mantegna* (Royal Academy of Arts, London; and the Metropolitan Museum of Art, New York: edited by Jane Martineau and with texts by Suzanne Boorsch, Keith Christiansen, David Ekserdjian, Charles Hope, David Landau and others, 1992). This catalogue assembles recent research and also recent disputes on Mantegna questions. In describing each work in this exhibition, different categories are used: "Andrea Mantegna", "attributed to Mantegna", "circle of Mantegna", "workshop of Mantegna" and "after Mantegna". In comparison with the examples of the 1992 catalogue, the present drawing does not have the "finished" or "mannered" characteristics of the group of works described there as "after Mantegna" (e.g. the *Virgin and Child* from the Hyde Collection, no. 19).

The attribution of part or all of this drawing to the hand of Andrea Mantegna would appear more plausible. This becomes apparent in comparing individual figures in this work with parallel figures in other drawings now assigned to the artist. In this drawing, the quality of the treatment of the body of the central standing youth, particularly the delicate modeling of the muscles of the torso, is very close to a number of similar works by Mantegna such as the figures in *Descent into Limbo* (Bibliothèque de l'Ecole Superièure des Beaux-Arts, Paris; *Mantegna,* London-New York, no.66). Furthermore, the sleeping figure on the right of the present drawing is comparable to the drawing *Man Lying on a Stone Slab* (*Mantegna*, The Trustees of the British Museum,London-New York, no. 43) with respect to the treatment of the legs, the draperies and the particular angle of the neck and head. The nature of the stance of the child in the drawing *Virgin and Child Enthroned with an Angel* (*Mantegna,* London-New York, no. 49) is

(text continues on page 20)

19

comparable to that of the child (or *amour*) at the far, lower-left of the present drawing. In another drawing of the *Virgin and Child* (Fondation Custodia - F. Lugt, Institut Nèerlandais, Paris; *Mantegna*, London-New York, no.53), the child is very close in technique and treatment to all four children in the present drawing and particularly to the child (in reverse) reaching over the wine vat.

Bacchanal with a Wine Vat, engraving, about 1940

In view of this drawing's relationship with the engraving *Bacchanal with a Wine Vat* (*Mantegna*, London-New York, no. 74), it is interesting to take into account the question of whether Mantegna himself executed the seven to nine or so engravings attributed to his hand or whether those works were executed by a *Premier Engraver* (or engravers) *after* Mantegna's original drawings. (On this question see: David Landau "Mantegna as Printmaker" and also Suzanne Boorsch "Mantegna and His Printmakers" in *Andrea Mantegna*, Royal Academy of Arts, London and The Metropolitan Museum of Art, New York, 1992: pp.56-67; R. Stanley Johnson " Mantegna", *Nouvelles de l'Estampe*, Bibliothèque Nationale, Paris, March, 1993: pp.50-52; and Keith Christiansen "The Case for Mantegna as Printmaker", *Burlington Magazine*, vol.135, Sept. 1993, pp. 604-612).

To achieve the extraordinary quality level of the engravings traditionally assigned to Mantegna, many years of apprenticeship would have been necessary. If he were the author of the actual engravings, Mantegna during those years of apprenticeship logically would have produced a certain number of engravings and, once his mastery of the medium reached a certain stage, logically he would have executed still others. The result is that the total Mantegna engraved oeuvre logically would have to consist of more than those now assigned to his hand. Adding to the questions on Mantegna's authorship of the engravings previously categorically assigned to his hand is the fact that Mantegna scholars, in spite of recent intensive efforts, have yet to find one single document to sustain Mantegna's authorship of the few engravings attributed to him (contrary for example to Dürer whose authorship of his own graphic works is proven by hundreds of contemporary documents). It thus has become increasingly difficult to continue to assign those engraved works to his hand until, beyond "expert opinions", some new substantial information is found. If in fact the engravings were not executed by Mantegna himself, they would have been executed after Mantegna or Mantegna-related drawings by an extremely competent member, or members, of his studio, an engraver or engravers who necessarily had a long and complete apprenticeship in that medium.

Now adding to this is the fact that a young archivist, Andrea Canova, doing research on the Gonzaga Family of Mantova, has discovered a contract of 1475 between Andrea Mantegna and an engraver named Gian Marco Cavalli. In this notarized contract, Andrea Mantegna requests Gian Marco Cavalli to produce engravings after a certain number of Mantegna's drawings.This is a further indication that the works, until recently catalogued as "Mantegna engravings", were not executed by Mantegna himself but rather by one of his assistants. This discovery of Canova was published in an article: "*Bella Scoperta : Mantegna disegnava ma non incideva*" (A Great Discovery : Mantegna Drew But Did Not Engrave) which appeared in the *ARTE* section of *IL SOLE-24 ORE*/5/III, 2000.

In conclusion, this present drawing appears to be one of several preparatory studies for the engraving or at least directly related to such a preparatory drawing. Originating from the workshop of Andrea Mantegna and apparently executed before the final form of the engraving, this drawing is particularly interesting as evidence of what appears to be an apparently hitherto unrecorded stage in the design process of the *Bacchanal with a Wine Vat.*

Collection:
Private Collection

7. GIULIO CLOVIO (attributed to)
Grizane, Croatia 1498 - 1578 Rome
After MICHELANGELO BUONARROTI
Caprese 1475-1564 Rome

A Bacchanal of Children, circa 1545-50
Dark red chalk used in a silver-point manner, on light tan paper
281 x 405 mm.; 11 x 16 inches

Watermark:
Ladder in a Circle (Roberts watermark Ladder-B)

Provenance:
A. Tardieu (Lugt 183b)
Nicos Dhikeos (with his stamp which is not in Lugt)

Notes:
1. This very complete, vivid, red chalk drawing, in remarkably fine overall condition, is a contemporary copy after Michelangelo's drawing *Bacchanal of Children at Windsor Castle* (see: A.E. Popham and Johannes Wilde *The Italian Drawings of the XV and XVI Centuries at Windsor Castle*, Johnson Reprint Corporation, New York, 1984, cat. no. 431 and pl. 28).

2. The *Ladder in Circle* watermark on this drawing (clearly visible after removal of the backing sheet) is identical to the Ladder-B watermark in: Jane Roberts, *A Dictionary of Michelangelo's Watermarks*, Olivetti, Milan, 1988, p. 23. Roberts notes that this watermark is found in Michelangelo's *The Annunciation* drawing at the Pierpont Morgan Library (Pierpont Morgan Library IV, 7; Charles de Tolnay, *Corpus dei disegni di Michelangelo*, Novara, 1975-80, no. 399) which she dates to the mid- to late 1540s. This watermark strongly supports the affirmation that the present drawing was made by an artist working in the immediate circle of Michelangelo.

3. In addition to the present drawing, there are at least three other contemporary drawings that display a similar technique of using the chalk in a silver-point manner. In his letter of May 10th, 1996, Paul Joannides has described the three works. One, in the Louvre (inv. 732, Wilde 67), after Michelangelo's *Christ on the Cross*, is in black chalk and was made for Michelangelo's friend Vittoria Colonna. It is dated by Joannides as circa 1540. On the mount of this drawing is an annotation by Philip Pouncey attributing it to Giulio Clovio. The attribution also has been accepted by both Catherine Monbeig-Goguel and Philippe Costamagna. Another drawing is the *Three Female Heads* in the Teylers Museum in Haarlem (inv. A13). This work, like Michelangelo's drawing of the subject, is in black chalk. On the mount is Catherine Monbeig-Goguel's annotation giving the drawing to Giulio Clovio. The third drawing (whereabouts unknown) was included as lot 82 in the Poynter Sale at Sotheby's on April 24, 1918. This is after Michelangelo's *Male Anatomy* at Windsor (Popham-Wilde No. 421) and has been assigned to Giulio Clovio by Wilde. In noting that all three of these sheets have been assigned to the hand of Giulio Clovio by well known authorities in the field: Phillip Pouncey, Catherine Monbeig-Goguel, Philippe Costamagna and Johannes Wilde, Joannides states that this fact would lead to "a strong supposition" that the present drawing also is by the same hand and thus by Clovio. Though of the opinion that all four drawings are by the same hand, Joannides still expresses skepticism as to their absolute attribution to Clovio rather than to possibly another talented artist in Michelangelo's immediate circle.

4. The present drawing, as is the case of the other three drawings in this grouping, is the same size as Michelangelo's corresponding drawing. The artist thus probably had access to the original. This would "tend to imply", as Joannides notes in his letter, "that the copyist was friendly with either Tommaso de' Cavalieri, who owned the drawing until his death in 1587, or with Michelangelo, or with both". In fact,

(text continues on page 24)

the original at Windsor is 274 x 388 mm. in size (but with the figures clearly slightly cut on left and rightand also vertically) while the present drawing is 281 x 405 mm. and appears to be the full image. This information further confirms Joannides' conclusion that the four drawings (including the present one) were executed by the same artist.

5. The present drawing, rather than Michelangelo's drawing of this subject, appears to be the original for an engraving executed by Enea Vico (1523-1567) and catalogued in *The New Bartsch* as no. 48: *Several Children Trying to Put a Stag into a Cooking Pot.* Vico's engraving is 286 x 405 mm., virtually identical to the present drawing (281 x 405 mm.). This engraving after the present drawing logically is in the reverse direction of the drawing. Nicolas Beatrizet (circa 1520-1570) executed a similar engraving, probably after Vico's. This latter work is therefore in the reverse direction of Vico's engraving but in the same direction as the original drawing and is 284 x 402 mm. in size. The nature of the execution of the present drawing, as well as that of the other three drawings in the same grouping, indicates that all four were executed by the same artist and possibly all as studies for engravings.

6. Michelangelo's own drawing of *Bacchanal of Children* was dated to October of 1533 by Popham and Wilde. This date is based on the fact that Raffaello da Montelupo (1504/1505-1566/1567), who first entered Michelangelo's service after the summer of 1533, at that time copied some of Michelangelo's sheets, including the *Bacchanal with Children*. As to the quality of Michelangelo's original drawing, Popham and Wilde state that:

> *...Technically the "Bacchanal with Children" represents the highest point of achievement in this series of "presentation sheets". It shows to a high degree the consistency and transparent texture of an engraving, and to perfection the closely-knit structure of a painting. Foreground and background are given the same amount of care as the figures, and there are practically no blank spaces left in the drawing.*

Michael Hirst notes that it is "...the evenness of tonality over the entire sheet that is the drawing's most astonishing aspect. The sheet is more consistently and comprehensively worked than any other of its kind." (*Michelangelo and His Drawings*, Yale University Press, New Haven, London, 1988, pp. 115-116).

Giorgio Vasari also was impressed with the quality of this drawing by Michelangelo. Vasari described Michelangelo's *Bacchanal of Children*, as the last of a group of four presentation drawings (the others being the *Rape of Ganymede*, the *Tityus* and the *Fall of Phaeton*) given to Michelangelo's close friend Tommaso de' Cavalieri (three of these drawings are in the British Royal Collections). Vasari was particularly taken up with the chiaroscuro effects in *Bacchanal of Children* which he described in 1550 (Vasari *Lives*, Barocchi edition, 1962, I. pp. 121-122): *col fiato non si farebbe piu d'union*e ("not with the fineness of breath could one have achieved greater unity") . In summing up the neo-platonic allusions of Michelangelo's four presentation drawings for Cavalieri, Erwin Panofsky wrote:

> *If the "Flight of Ganymede" symbolizes the enraptured ascension of the Mind, and if again the "Punishment of Tityus" and the "Fall of Phaeton" exemplify the fate of those who are incapable of controlling their sensuality and imagination, the "Children's Bacchanal", which is entirely devoid of amorous tension, might be the image of a still lower sphere: the sphere of a purely vegetative life which is as much beneath specifically human dignity as the Mind is above specifically human limitations. (Panofsky, Studies in Iconology, Icon Editions, New York, 1967, p. 223).*

The *Bacchanal of Children* in fact appears to be the most complex and enigmatic of the four presentation drawings made for Cavalieri (Michelangelo made other drawings for Cavalieri including his *Cleopatra*). The central group in this drawing shows seven *putti* carrying what appears to be the body of a deer. At the upper-left, there is a group of nine other *putti* around a large cauldron above which are seen the heads of a pig and a hare. At the upper right, a group of *putti* are drinking from what appears to be a wine vat. Lower left is a woman-satyr with children and lower right several *putti* apparently unveiling a naked man. Until now, there has been no completely convincing interpretation of the whole scene.

7. In considering the attribution of the present drawing to Giulio Clovio, comparisons could be made with Clovio works included in Joannides' recent book on Windsor's Michelangelo drawings (*Michelangelo and His Influence: Drawings from Windsor Castle*, National Gallery of Art, Washington, D.C.,1996). In this publication, the Clovio drawings *Head of Minerva* (circa 1540, cat. no. 5), *Ganymede* (circa 1540, cat. no. 15) and *The Virgin and Child with Saints...*(circa 1537, cat. no. 22) all have a finished, realistic quality and technique which differs markedly from the present drawing. On the other hand, the later drawings, also attributed to Clovio by Joannides, such as *Christ on the Cross* (circa 1545, cat. no. 25) and the red chalk drawing after Michelangelo *The Flagellation* (circa 1545, cat. no. 34) are apparently closer in date and certainly closer in technique and treatment to the present drawing. These and other comparisons, together with the related opinions noted above of Costamagna, Monbeig-Goguel, Pouncy and Wilde, as well as the circa 1545 *Ladder in Circle-B* watermark, support a date of circa 1545-50 and an attribution of the present drawing to Giulio Clovio.

8. VENICE MASTER

St. Vincent Ferrere Kneeling Before the Virgin and Child, Venice, about 1540

Miniature on the frontispiece of a Ducale on vellum: 225 x 155 mm.; 8 7/8 x 6 1/8 inches

Provenance:
1. This is the frontispiece of a Ducale issued by Pietro Lando (who was Doge of Venice 1537-1543) to a member of the Ghisi family of Venice.
2. William Young Ottley (1771-1836). Included in the sale of the Ottley Collection in 1838 (Sotheby's May 12, 1838: lot 228 where catalogued as "by Beneditto Bordone, about 1538") and where sold for f. 1.11s to "Rodd for Holford".
3. Robert Stayner Holford (1808-1892): Holford catalogue, no. 75, plate LXIX. A.N.L. Munby: *Connoisseurs and Medieval Miniatures,* 1972, p. 147 described Holford:

   > If one wished to depict an Ideal Connoisseur the result might well resemble Robert Holford. With his long hair, imperial beard, wide brimmed hat, and much be-frogged cloak he looked more like a spruce Dante Rossetti than a millionaire who changed the appearance of central London by erecting Park Lane and his vast Italianate palace, Dorchester House.

4. Sir George Holford (1860-1926). Acquired by descent from Robert Stayner Holford.
5. Edwards Collection, from the George Holford Collection Sale July 12, 1927, lot 47.

Notes:
1. The Virgin is shown seated by a classical pillar with the Child on her lap pointing towards St. Vincent. St. Vincent, kneeling, holds flames, a triple lily and a book. All is set with a landscape background. The miniature is in an oval cartouche 90 x 100mm. with the Venetian Lion of St. Mark below. There is a full border of gold and colored flowers on a pale blue ground with vignettes of Justice (in a classical landscape) and two classical maidens (in *camaieu d'or*). The arms of Ghisi of Venice are suspended in a landscape and flanked by his initials "V.G." together with the opening of the text in a central panel in gold capitals (with some offsetting of the script below the miniature) on a red ground.
2. Over the centuries, this subject traditionally has been indicated as St. Anthony of Padua. Part of this mistake was caused by the fact that St. Anthony and St. Vincent were both dressed as Dominicans. St. Anthony, however, is usually depicted with the Christ Child in his arms, while St. Vincent is never depicted with the Christ Child in his arms. In this case, with the typical flames in his hands (these are also sometimes on his head), the subject of this work could only be St. Vincent Ferrere.

9. CHERUBINO ALBERTI
Borgo San Sepolcro 1553-1615 Rome

La Sibilla persica
The Persian Sibyl

Engraving after Michelangelo Buonarroti (Caprese 1475 - 1564 Rome) : 425 x 280 mm.; 16 3/4 x 11 in.

Reference: Bartsch 74

Notes:
1. A strong impression of this engraving after Michelangelo's treatment of this subject in the Sistine Chapel. Michelangelo executed his frescos for the Sistine Chapel between 1508 and 1512. Surrounding the enormous *Last Judgement,* he painted a series of prophets and sibyls including the *Persian Sibyl* and also a series of "history" panels from *Genesis.* Alberti then later executed a number of engravings after various subjects in Michelangelo's Sistine Chapel. In addition to the *Persian Sibyl*, these included *One of the Saved* from the *Last Judgement* (Bartsch XVII.75.68). In this and other engravings, Alberti, making use of the lessons of earlier masters such as Cornelis Cort (1533 - 1578), developed a decoratively effective engraving style (see: Michael Bury *The Print in Italy 1550 - 1620,* The British Museum press, 2001: p. 125).
2. Active in San Sepolcro and Rome, Alberti was a painter, engraver and cross-bow constructor. His earliest engravings date from 1571 and he continued as a printmaker until 1590. Bury (ref. above p. 221) notes that Alberti executed..." Mythological, devotional and ornemental subjects, portraits and antiquities". Over the decades, Alberti executed prints after Raphael, Michelangelo, Polidoro da Caravaggio, Andrea del Sarto, Rosso Fiorentino, Taddeo and Federico Zuccaro. Similar in ways to the situation of Luca Bertelli (active in Padua and Venice between 1564 and 1589), Alberti kept control over most of his own plates and made the decisions concerning their printing. (see our no.5, note 3).

10. THE MASTER FG (active around 1530-1560)
(François Gentil?)

Alexandra with Talestrius, circa 1530

Engraving after Francesco Primaticcio (Bologna 1504-1570 Paris) : 242 x 242 mm.; 9 1/2 x 9 1/2 inches

Provenance:
Chatsworth Collection (Dukes of Devonshire)
The Chatsworth Settlement, Christies, London, Dec. 5, 1985: no. 106

Notes:
1. A very fine and rare impression. The School of Fontainebleau influence quite evident. Beside the monogram, there is an inscription: "A-Fontana-Bleo-Bol", the "Bol" apparently referring to Primaticcio, known as il Bolognese, on one of whose works this print could have been based.
2. As the Master FG, Nagler suggests Guido Ruggieri who went to Fontainebleau with Primaticcio around1531. Ruggieri was born in Bologna and was actively involved in printmaking around 1550. His prints are generally signed with a G" and an "R" interlaced weith an "F" (for *fecit*). F. Hebet, on the other hand, has proposed the sculptor/engraver Françoois Gentil (Troyes circa 1510 - 1588 Troyes). Henri Zerner in his *L'École de Fontainebleau* exhibit catalogue of 1972 (p. 291) states that so far no positive identification has been possible for the Master FG.

(illustrated on page 8)

Cum priuilegio Summi Pontificis

29

11. PAOLO FARINATI
Verona 1524-1606 Verona

The Triumph of Constantine the Great, about 1556-1558

Pen and brown ink and black chalk
445 x 330 mm; 17 1/2 x 13 inches
Inscribed on the verso: EE 27/10

Notes:

1. Farinati, a student of Niccolo Giolfino and A. Badile, also had studied the works of Parmigianino, Tiziano, Giorgione and particularly Giulio Romano. In this magnificent drawing, there are numerous exact parallels seen in many of Farinati's etchings. This artist's peculiar treatment of hands is seen in virtually everyone of his prints reproduced in *The Illustrated Bartsch* (Vol. 32, New York, 1979: pp. 259-269). The treatment of the "cupids" in the upper-left of this drawing is paralleled by the putti in Farinati's *The Drunken Satyr (Illus. Bartsch* p. 267).

2. Farinati's son, Horazio Farinati (1559-c. 1616), was a student of his father. A number of his paintings, including the *Descent from the Cross*, now in the church of St. Paul in Verona, were virtually exact copies of his father's works. In addition, Horazio's engravings were all executed directly after his father's drawings. In this respect, this drawing by Paolo Farinati appears to be the inspiration for Horazio's *Scene of Battle* engraving (*Illus. Bartsch*, no. 6, p. 274), in which there is the identical and idiosyncratic presentation of several of the figures and horses.

3. Professor Jack Freiberg, in his letter of April 14, 1995, notes that this drawing relates to a painting on which he then was working. The painting, documented as 1556-58, is found in the church of Santa Maria in Organo in Verona. Professor Freiberg indicates that the subject of this painting and the drawing, Constantine the Great, according to tradition was "stricken by leprosy and advised by pagan priests that to be healed he had to bathe in the blood of three thousand infants. He renounced this cure when confronted with the pitiful cries of the mothers...". These pleading mothers are depicted on the upper-left of this drawing as well as on the painting in Santa Maria in Organo in Verona.

4. Jack Freiberg in: *The Lateran in 1600: Christian Concord in Counter-Reformation Rome* (Cambridge, 1995) points out (footnote 32, p. 224) that Farinati's painting in Santa Maria in Organo in Verona "makes explicit the underlying significance of the episode as a testament to Constantine's proto-Christian virtue by pairing the scene with the *Massacre of the Innocents*. Freiberg also notes (footnote 34, p. 224) that "The triumphal carriage was traditionally drawn by four white horses", but that "in the visual traditional two horses are sometimes substituted."

5. Additional information, related to the drawing, on this painting (and its pendant *Massacre of the Innocents*) can be found in: Giorgio Vasari (Milanesi ed.), 6:374-5; Giuseppe Gerola, *Le antiche pale di S. Maria in Organo di Verona* (Bergamo, 1913),20 n. 11; and Paolo Carpeggiani, "Paolo Farinati," in *Maestri della pittura veronese*, ed. Pierpaolo Brugnoli, Verona, 1974, 233, figs. 162-3.

12. GIORGIO GHISI

Mantua 1520-1582 Mantua

The Judgement of Paris (2nd State), 1555

Engraving after Giovanni Battista Bertani (1516-1576)
395 x 522 mm.; 15 9/16 x 20 9/16 inches

Reference: Bartsch XV, 60; Heller-Anderson 18; Boorsch, Lewis and Lewis 16-II/III

Provenance:
Sir Joshua Reynolds (Lugt 2364)
A. N. Champernowne (Lugt 153)

Notes:
1. A superb, richly inked impression, printed with considerable tone. This is an extremely rare, early proof of the 2nd State (of three states) before the changes in the cliff behind Minerva's head (2 pairs of birds added in the sky besides the addtion of the two other birds to upper right in the larger sky area), and before the addition of the inscription on the tablet lower left. There are no known 1st or 2nd State impressions of this work in any U.S. museum or private collection. Boorsch, Lewis and Lewis (*The Engravings of Giorgio Ghisi*, The Metropolitan Museum of Art, Suzanne Boorsch, Michal and R. E. Lewis , New York, 1985) record only one known impression of the 1st State (Fitzwillian Museum, Cambridge) and only one of the 2nd State (The Albertina, Vienna). To these two early impressions must be added this present impression.
2. *The Judgement of Paris* is one of five engravings which Ghisi produced while in the employ of Hieronymus Cock (who also published many of the works after Bruegel) in Antwerp between 1550 and 1555. The drawing by Bertani, on which this engraving is based, is in the Musei Civici del Castello Visconteo in Pavia and is of a size and direction very close to the engraving. Bertani's drawing in turn very likely could have been based on Marcantonio Raimondi's engraving of a design of the subject made by Raphael. Bertani's drawing also is very parallel to the work after Giulio Romano, *The Feast for Cupid and Psych* in the Palazzo del Te in Mantua. As to the direct relationship between Bertani's drawing and this Ghisi engraving, see also: *Giorgio Ghisi: An Introduction* by Suzanne Boorsch (*Print Collector's Newsletter,* July-August, 1985: p. 87).
3. It is to be noted that Ghisi's native Mantua had been the home of Andrea Mantegna who had served the ruling Gonzaga family from about 1460 until Mantegna's death in 1506. In about 1524, when Ghisi was four years old, another major artist Giulio Romano, the follower of Raphael, came to Mantua to take charge of the Gonzaga's world of art. In 1549, taking over Romano's position, Giovanni Battista Bertani became Mantua's art director and remained so until his death in 1576. It is thus logical to feel that Ghisi had been indirectly influenced by the traditions of Mantegna and Raphael as well as by the direct presence of Romano and Bertani.
4. This engraving carries one of the most famous of all collector's marks, that of the painter Sir Joshua Reynolds (1723-1792). Reynolds brought together a fabulous collection of paintings, drawings and prints. Few artists, outside of Rembrandt, have been such avid and insatiable collectors. The second collector's mark on this work, that of A. M. Champernowne (born in 1871), refers to an early twentieth century collector whose extensive print collection concentrated particularly on works by Rembrandt, Van Ostade and Claude Gellée Lorrain.

Collection:
Private Collection

13. BARTOLOMEO CORIOLANO
Bologna about 1599 - 1676 Bologna

A Sibyl, after Guido Reni (Calvenzano 1575-1642 Bologna)

Chiaroscuro woodcut printed in bluish gray and black on cream laid paper
305 x 220 mm.; 12 x 8 5/8 inches

Reference:
1. Bartsch XII, no. 4
2. "Incisori Bolognesi ed Emiliani del sec. XVII", *Catalogo Generale della raccolta di stampe antiche,* Pinacoteca Nazionale di Bologna, 1973: Sezione III, no. 355.

Note:
A very fine impression , with strong colors, of this rare chiaroscuro woodcut. In this work, Coriolano follows in the *chiaroscuro* woodcut tradition established in Venice and Rome by Ugo da Carpi (1480 - circa 1532). See: no. 2 by Ugo da Carpi in this publication.

14-17. ANTONIO TEMPESTA
Florence 1555 - 1630 Rome

Four Stages of Life (Aetas Aurea, Aetas Argentea, Aetas Aenea and *Aetas Ferrea)*, 1599

The set of four etchings: each 207 x 337 mm.; 8 1/8 x 13 1/4 inches

Each with watermark:
Anchor in Circle

References:
Bartsch 1329-1332

Notes:
1.   Superb, well contrasted impressions of this very rare complete set. To be noted is that the guidelines for the text, no longer visible after just a few impressions, are very strong here and correspond to the earliest possible impressions.
2.   Bury (Michael Bury *The Print in Italy 1550 - 1620,* British Museum, London, 2001: p. 89) refers to Tempesta's "extraordinary range of invention in the movements and gestures of men and horses...The sense of dynamic speed that he could communicate through his handling of the etching process gave his work an immense appeal to many artists...".Among enthusiasts for the etchings of Tempesta were Rubens and Rembrandt. Rembrandt's etchings *The Large Lion Hunt* (Bartsch 114) and *The Small Lion Hunt* (Bartsch 115), for examples, were directly inspired by Tempesta's two earlier and similarly treated subjects (Tempesta ref. Bartsch 1132 and 1171).

(not illustrated)

18. LUCA BERTELLI
Active in Padua and Venice between 1564 and 1598

Filiberto di Scialon, Prince of Orange, On Horseback

Etching : 224 x 187 mm.; 8 7/8 x 7 3/8 inches

Watermark:*Sea-Siren in Circle with Six-Sided Star* (Heawood 3800). Heawood dates 1562, Venice.

Reference: Meyer, *Allgemeines Künstler Lexikon III*, 703, 48.

Notes:
1. A strong, early and rare impression of this portrait of the Prince of Orange with his *Coat of Arms* below. In this dramatic depiction, the rider and his horse both stare fiercely into the eyes of the onlooker. The upright, formal position of the prince and the well-trained stance of the horse, their disciplined grace and elegance, all bespeak of a well- established and powerful sixteenth- century noble family.
2. Luca Bertelli was a printmaker, book and print dealer and publisher. He published prints by Agostino Carracci, Giacomo Franco and Martino Rota as well as after Michelangelo, Veronese, Titian, Domenico Campagnola, Raphael, Farinati and Clovio. In many cases, we cannot be sure of the nature or participation of Bertelli himself as a printmaker. The line between financial and working relationships between Bertelli and his projects is often unclear. Bury (Michael Bury *The Print in Italy 1550-1620*, The British Museum Press, 2001) has analysed many of these (with respect to Bertelli directly, see Bury: pp. 69, 74-77, 109, 115, 170-174, 179, 222 and no. 64). An example of the complications of attribtion questions concerns Agostino Carracci's (1557-1602) very large engraving on two sheets (451 x 592 mm. and 459 x 592 mm.) of 1582: *The Martyrdom of Saint Giustina* of Padua after a Paolo Veronese painting in the church of Santa Giustina in Padua. The inscription below this work is: *..Addictissimi Lucus Bertullus, et socius.* It would be difficult to imagine that Agostino Carricci stayed in Bertelli's workshop long enough to have alone completed this enormous project. How much did Bertelli himself contribute to the actual engraving? Who were the partners (*socius*) involved and what involvement did they have? Concerning this specific work, see: Diane DeGrazia Bohlin *Prints and Related Drawings by the Carracci Family,* National Gallery of Art, Washington, D.C., 1979: no. 105, pp.204-206.

19. MARIO CARTARO
Active in Rome 1560-1588

Admiranda beati aurelii Augustini
The People Render Their Admiration for the Blessed Augustin

Engraving: 393 x 507mm.; 15 7/16 x 20 1/8 inches

Notes:
This fascinating and major engraving is so rare that it apparently was never seen by either Bartsch or Passavant. Even Nagler (*Die Monogrammisten I*) does not mention this work.The subject of this engraving is Augustin of Hippo (354-430), one of the greatest Church Fathers. In the upper part of this grandiose scene and accompanied by a group of spirtiual leaders, Augustinus is being taken by boat across a sea. In the foreground, a group of heretics is being led into Hell. In the middle-ground, winding from one side of the sheet to the other, a long line of True Believers, desiring to pay homage to Christ on the Cross, is depicted moving toward the upper left of the scene. The multiple iconographic aspects depicted in this moment in the life of Augustinus are complex and difficult to decipher.

(not illustrated)

FILIBERTO DI SCIALON
PRINCIPE DI ORANGE.

L'alma cittade; in cui sepolta giace
Parthenope Sirena in riua al mare;
Dal gran furore del Lotrecco audace
Difesi, e trassi di miserie amare;

Indi di Flora, a cui spiacea la pace
D'Italia, con mie forze inuitte, e chiare
Sottoposi al gran Cesare, et a Roma
L'alta potenza in picciol tempo doma.

20. CARLO MARATTA
Camerano 1625-1713 Rome

Madonna and Child and Saint with Two Angels, about 1680

Red chalk on a green-blue paper, with rounded top
422 x 275 mm.; 16 5/8 x 10 7/8 inches

Provenance:
Collector's mark, lower center (not in Lugt)

Notes:
1. This confidently executed drawing is a study related to Maratta's painting *La Vergine appare a S.Stanislao Kotska* 1687 in the second chapel to the right, in the church of S. Andrea al Quirinale in Rome (see: Amalia Mezzetti "Contributi a Carlo Maratti", no. 93 on page 333 in : *Rivista dell'Istituto Nazonale d'Archeologia e Storia dell'Arte,* vol. 4, 1955). Mezzetti (ref. above, pp. 352-53 *Appendice-Documenti inediti*) records the original contract of September 22, 1679 in which Maratta agreed to terminate this painting for the Cappella del Beato Stanislao in one year for "scudi 100 o altra somma che havessi presa". In spite of this contract, Maratta did not finish this painting until 1687. Mezzetti (ref. above) records Maratta's note stating that, on September 19, 1687, he received "Scudi Trecento" from the "mano del P. Giuseppe Tonini della Compagnia di Giusù"(sic) and that Father Tonini was "interamente sodisfatto" (see: *Fondo Gesuitico al Gesù di Roma*-S. Andrea al Quirinale Filza 865, fascicolo 13).
2. Two other drawings related to this commission are in the Düsseldorf Kunstmuseum (Ann Sutherland Harris and Eckhard Schaar *Die Handzeichnungen von Andrea Sacchi und Carlo Maratta,* Düsseldorf, 1967, vol. I, nos. 348 and 349). This particular drawing could be compared to a number of other Maratta drawings formerly from Lambert Krahe's (1712-1790) extensive collection, most of which now are in the Düsseldorf Kunstmuseum. One of these (*Facetten des Barock: Meisterzeichnungen von Gianlorenzo Bernini bis Anton Raphael Mengs aus dem Kunstmuseum Düsseldorf* Akademiesammlung, Düsseldorf, 1990 cat. no. 35 "Study of a Tree Nymph", about 1680) shows a very similar use of red chalk on a green-blue paper with a rounded top as well as a similar treatment of a woman's head. Another of these (ref. above, cat. no. 36 "Head of a Woman with Two Studies of Hands", about 1695) shows a virtually identical and highly personal treatment of the hand as seen in the left hand of the Madonna in the present drawing.

21. FRA BONAVENTURA BISI (also known as "il Padre pitturino")
Bologna 1612 - 1659 Bologna

The Holy Family, 1634

Etching after Parmigianino (Parma 1503 - 1540 Casal Maggiore): 305 x 230 mm.; 12 x 9 inches

Reference:
Nagler *Monogrammisten II,* 1956
De Vesme 1 III

Notes:
1. A strong and harmonius impression of this extremely rare work. The elegance and fluidity of the drawing technique, so evident in this work, as well the assured handling of this classical subject are excellent representations of the spirit and very soul of the Italian Renaissance. Nagler states that this work has been inspired by a work by Parmagianino. De Vesme, on the other hand, is not sure that the creator of this work was Bisi and also thought that the artist's inspiration came rather from a work by Giorgio Vasari. Our description agrees with Nagler who assigns this work to Bisi after Parmigianino.
2. It is to be noted that Bisi was a Franciscan monk who was a student of Lucio Massari and, above all, was a miniaturist . He also was a "renaissance man" whose erudition won him the task of putting together the art collection of Duke Alfons IV of Modena.

22. NICOLAS CHAPRON
Châteaudun 1612 - 1656 Paris

L'alliance de Bacchus et Vénus, 1639
The Union of Bacchus and Venus

Etching: 314 x 392 mm.; 12 x 15 1/2 inches

Provenance: With the address of Mariette

Reference: Robert-Dumesnil 58-III

Notes:
A strong, well contrasted and rare, early impression of this intriguing subject.
(not illustrated)

23. HENRI MAUPERCHE
Paris c.1602 - 1686 Paris

The Birth of Christ - With the Praying Shepherds

Engraving: 221 x 298 mm.; 8 7/8 x 11 3/4 inches

Reference: Robert-Dumesnil 18-II

Notes:
A fine impression. With the address of P. Giffart. Mauperche produced over fifty engravings.
(not illustrated)

41

24. GIOVANNI BENEDETTO CASTIGLIONE
Genova 1616 - about 1665 Mantova

Circe Changing Odysseus' Men into Beasts, about 1651

Etching
217 x 307 mm.; 8 1/2 x 12 1/8 inches

Watermark:
An unidentified watermark

Reference:
Bartsch 22

Notes:
1. A fine impression of one of the major prints produced in seventeenth-century Italy.
2. Ann Percy (*Castiglione*, Philadelphia Museum of Art, 1971) points out that in this etching as well as in Castiglione's *Noah and the Animals Entering the Ark*, the use of Rembrandtesque chiaroscuro is rather tight and dense in comparison to the more diffuse and evocative effects of the etchings of the late forties. Percy concludes that this etching fits in somewhere after the mid-fifties.
3. It is to be noted that the book at Circe's feet seems to be covered with astrological symbols and that there appears to be a magic wand in her hand. As told by Thomas Bulfinch in his essay "Odysseus and Circe" (from: *Encyclopedia Mythica*, edition 1995), Circe, daughter of the sun, was a sorceress best known for her ability to turn men into animals with her wand and renowned for her knowledge of magic and poisonous herbs. It also seems that she had powers for spiritual purification and it was she who purified the Argonauts in preparation for the murder of Apsyrtus. Circe is particularly remembered for her encounter with Odysseus and his men. After Odysseus landed in Aeaea, his crew later met with Circe and were turned into pigs. Circe's spells, however, had no effect on Odysseus who earlier was given an herb by Hermes to resist her power. Circe realizing that she was powerless over him lifted the spell from the crew and welcomed them into her home. Circe and Odysseus eventually bore a child together named Telegonus who later ruled over the Tyrsenians.
4. Russell and Barnes (H. Diane Russell with Bernardine Barnes, *Eva/Ave: Women in Renaissance and Baroque Prints*, National Gallery of Art, Washington, Feminist Press at the City of New York, 1990: p. 171) refer to Sueda Manning's essay "The Transformation of Circe: The Significance of the Sorceress Subject in 17th Century Genovese Painting" (*Scritti di storia dell'arte in onore de Federico Zeri*, Electa Editrice-The J. Paul Getty Trust, 1984). Sueda Manning sees here "the beginning of Castiglione's amalgamation of the sorceress theme with that of the Vanitas theme...Castiglione's message comes to center on the futility of all human endeavors, as time destroys even the powers of the sorceress."

II
German and Dutch
Prints and Drawings 1500-1700

25. ALBRECHT DÜRER
Nuremberg 1471 - 1528 Nuremberg

Nemesis, 1502 (also called *Fortuna* or *Das grosse Glück*)

Engraving
329 x 224 mm.; 12 7/8 x 8 3/4 inches

Watermark: *High Crown* (Meder 20)

References:
Meder 72-IIa

Notes:
1. A very fine and very rare Meder-IIa impression of this extraordinary engraving. It is the high point arrived at by Dürer in rendering the nude body in the period before his second voyage to Italy. This was before his *Adam and Eve* engraving of 1504 and his then new-found use of constructed proportions. This work, with its bird-eye view of the mountains below, also represents a significant advance in the "realistic" treatment of landscape in Western art. Although the landscape in this scene had been described by Sandrart in 1675 as representing the village in Hungary where Dürer's father had been born, it now is generally agreed that the scene is a view of Chiusa (Klausen) in the Val d'Isarco in the Tyrol (south Austria) seen in "mirror image". This could have been based on a now lost sketch or watercolor which Dürer could have executed during his first journey to Italy in 1495-1496. From Dürer's diary, it is clear that by 1520 the *Nemesis* already was considered as one of his most exceptional works (see: Dürer's *Record of Journeys to Venice and the Low Countries*, Dover Publications, 1995).
2. Meder-IIa impressions have a vertical scratch added to the middle of the bridge in the landscape and the earliest of these impressions are on *High Crown* (M.20) watermarked paper . These early impressions as seen here also have the dotted clouds lower center quite visible, plus a burr effect seen particularly in the feathers and the dark mountains.
3. Some interesting comments over the years on this work are the following:

> 1568 - Vasari:...*He engraved also a nude figure floating in the clouds, representing "Temperantia" with magnificent wings, a golden cup, and reins in her hands...*
>
> 1675 - Sandrart:...*The landscape below is supposedly the village called Eytar, near Wardein in Hungary, the birthplace of Dürer's father.*
>
> 1808 - Bartsch:...*The face is perhaps a likeness of Dürer's wife, Agnes.*
>
> 1827- Heller:...*Rare in prime impressions which are distinguished by small dot-like clouds near the top, missing on later impressions.*
>
> 1861- Hausmann:...*Early strong impressions of this work ... are all on "High Crown" (M. 20) paper...superior to those with the "Bull's Head" watermark.*
>
> 1876- Thausing was perhaps the first to really understood the importance of Dürer's *Nemesis: With this powerful feminity, the nordic cult of nature triumphantly first enters the history of art. Everything is sacrificed, including whatever we might call beautiful according to ancient aesthetic formalism, for the sake of truth. In spite of it, our feeling are not violated and admit the genuineness of these forms, the fullness of life exuded by these limbs. It is the high point reached by Dürer in rendering the nude body without prejudice before he was influenced by constructed proportions.*

26. ALBRECHT DÜRER
Nürnberg 1471-1528 Nürnberg

Der verlorene Sohn, about 1496
The Prodigal Son

Engraving:
248 x 190 mm.; 9 3/4 x 7 3/8 inches

Watermark:
Gotisches P (M. 322). In Dürer engravings, Meder dates this watermark from 1500 to about 1514 and notes it in "the earliest impressions after those with either *Ox's Head* [M. 62] or *High Crown* [M. 20] watermarks" (*...In den frühesten Stichen nach Ochsenkopf und Hohe Krone...*). This same watermark is also found on early impressions of Dürer's engraving *St. Jerome in the Desert* (Meder 57) of 1496-1497.

Provenance:
F. von Hagens (Lugt 1052a)
André-Jean Hachette, Paris (Lugt 132)

Reference:
Meder 28b

Notes:
1. A fine, Meder b impression of one of Dürer's most important engravings. Meder's description of the earliest possible "a" impressions of this work would show strong, vertical scratches on the body of the pig to the right foreground and on the large gabled roof to the upper right. According to Meder, these scratches are very visible on the Meder "b" impressions, such as this one, but then largely (completely in the case of the roof) disappear in the "c" impressions.
2. This scene with *The Prodigal Son* is from a parable in the *New Testament* (Luke 15/11-24), describing when the prodigal son had been abased to be in the fields "to feed the swine". Panofsky (Erwin Panofsky, *Albrecht Dürer,* Princeton University Press, 1971 edition: p.76) notes that in this work, Dürer made two major iconographical changes. First, the scene is not staged in the fields, but rather in a farmyard, creating "an atmosphere of genuine, yet intensely poetic rusticity". Secondly, according to Panofsky (taking a phrase from Giorgio Vasari's description of this same work), the scene "...is balanced by an increase in pathos : the prodigal son no longer stands by the swine with mournful composure, but has gone to his knees in their very midst, wringing his hands in bitter remorse". At the same time that the son "abases himself to the level of beasts, he raises his eyes and his thoughts to the heaven of God".
3. Provenance includes Franz von Hagens (1817-1899), from Düsseldorf and Dresden, who in his time assembled one of the great old master print collections (particularly Dürer and Rembrandt). Another former owner was André-Jean Hachette (born in Paris, 1873), a passionate collector of 15th/16th century prints. Hachette's collection was sold in Paris on June 11, 1953 (including this work as lot no. 6).

27. LUCAS VAN LEYDEN
Leyden 1494-1553 Leyden

Ecce Homo (1st State), 1510

Engraving: 288 x 454 mm.; 11 3/8 x 18 in.

Watermark:
Gotisches P (Hollstein watermark no. 25)

Provenance:
Raphael Esmerian

Reference:
Hollstein 71-I/III
J. P. Filedt Kok, *Lucas van Leyden - grafiek,* Rijksprentenkabinet, Rijksmuseum, Amsterdam, 1978: see no. 24/a-b and p. 120.
Ellen S. Jacobowitz and Stephanie L. Stepanek *The Prints of Lucas van Leyden and His Contemporaries,* National Gallery of Art, Washington 1983: no. 30, pages 96-97.

Notes:
1. A superb impression. The printing in all areas of this proof is exceptionally well-balanced and crisp.
2. Hollstein dates this *Gotisches P* watermark between 1508 and 1510 and states that this watermark is found on early impressions of this work.
3. This engraving by van Leyden has been of great influence over the centuries. Particularly notable is Rembrandt's drypoint of 1655, *Presentation of Christ to the People* (Bartsch no. 76), which represents a direct borrowing from van Leyden's 1510 composition.
4. Jacobowitz and Stepanek (reference above pp. 96-97), referring to Peter Parshall, "Lucas van Leyden's Narrative Style," *Nederlands Kunsthistorisch Jaarboek 29* (1978): 216-218, note that:

> Once again Lucas has reversed the traditional compostional formula, placing Christ in a subordinate position while emphasizing the crowd. Such reversals had become standard in his work by this time, reflecting his preoccupation with presenting religion in the most immediate human terms. This emphasis on humanity, on the people's shared responsibility rather than Christ's suffering, would later exemplify much of Reformation theology.
>
> Contemporaneity and temporality are carried to an unusual extreme here, almost to the point of overwhelming the basic spiritual nature of the subject. The sense of ordinary daily activity is fostered by numerous figures casually meandering through the square, or participating in formal conversation. The artist's own sixteenth century milieu is evoked by the attire: Renaissance armor, Oriental turbans, Turkish archers' costumes, and Jewish cloaks. But most important, the vast architectural setting, noted for its perspectival accuracy and exceptional elaborateness, actually derives from the real town square located in Leiden.

28. ALBRECHT DÜRER

Nürnberg 1471- 1528 Nürnberg

The Adoration of the Lamb, circa 1497

Woodcut: Latin text edition of 1511
393 x 281 mm.; 15 1/2 x 11 1/8 inches

Reference:
Bartsch 67
Meder 176

Notes:

1. A fine, early and rare impression from the Latin text edition from 1511 of this splendid subject. This sheet appears to be one of the first of the series of works which eventually became *The Apocalypse*. In the form of a fine, life-time impression, this also appears to be one of the rarest.

2. The biblical reference here is *Revelation* 5: (6):

    > And I beheld and, lo, in the midst of the throne and of the four living beasts, and in the midst of the elders, stood a Lamb as though it had been slain, having seven horns and seven eyes, which are the seven spirits of God sent forth to all the earth. 14: (1) And I looked and, lo, a Lamb stood on Mount Zion, and with him a hundred and forty-four thousand, having his father's name written on their foreheads. (3) And they sang, as it were, a new song before the throne and before the four living beasts and the elders, 19: (4) And the four and twenty elders and the four living beasts fell down and worshipped God that sat on the throne, saying Amen, Hallelujah! (10) And I fell at his feet to worship, him. And he said to me: See thou, do it not! I am thy fellow servant. 7:(9) After this I beheld and, lo, a great multitude, which no man could number, of all nations and kindreds and peoples and tongues, stood before the throne and before the Lamb, clothed with white robes and palms in their hands, (10) and I cried with a loud voice, saying, Salvation to our God, who sitteth upon the throne and unto the Lamb. (13) And one of the elders answered, saying unto me, Who are these who are arrayed in white robes? And from where did they come?

29. LUCAS VAN LEYDEN
Leyden 1494-1553 Leyden

Herod Receives the Head of St. John the Baptist, 1514

Woodcut
411 x 292 mm.; 16 1/4 x 11 1/2 inches

Reference:
Hollstein 21-I-(from II)
J. P. Filedt Kok, *Lucas van Leyden - grafiek,* Rijksprentenkabinet, Rijksmuseum, Amsterdam, 1978: no. 78, repr. p. 61 (impression of the Albertina, Vienna).
Ellen S. Jacobowitz and Stephanie L. Stepanek *The Prints of Lucas van Leyden and His Contemporaries,* National Gallery of Art, Washington 1983 no. 36, page 115.

Notes:
1. A superb impression. Except for traces of folds, seen from verso, in almost perfect condition. The rareness of this work is indicated by the fact that, between 1876 and 1930, Hollstein was able to discover only ten proofs of this woodcut.
2. The story of Herod and St. John the Baptist, as depicted here by Lucas van Leyden, is told in several places in the Bible. One is in Matthew 14,3-12, while another is found in Mark 6, 17-29:

> Herod was the one who had John arrested and bound in prison on account of Herodias, the wife of his brother Philip, whom he had married. John had said to Herod: "It is not lawful for you to have your brother's wife". Herodias harboured a grudge against him [John] and wanted to kill him. She had the opportunity one day when Herod, on his birthday, gave a banquet...Herodias's own daughter [Salomé] came in and performed a dance that delighted Herod and his guests. The king said to the girl: "Ask of me whatever you wish and I will grant it to you...even half of my kingdom". She went out and said to her mother: "What shall I ask for?" Her mother replied: "The head of John the Baptist". The girl hurried back to the king and made her request: "I want you to give me at once on a platter the head of John the Baptist"...[The king] promptly dispatched an executioner ...who brought in the head on a platter and gave it to the girl..who in turn gave it to her mother.

3. Jacobowitz & Stepanek (reference above, page 115) note that:

> Lucas was unique in using the subject pictorially within a *Power of Women* group. The complicitous roles played by the two women is a key to the woodcut's - indeed the series'- theme, the evil grasp women hold over men. Salomé's gliding pose with fluttering sash recalls the suggestive, alluring nature of her dance. The knife held by Herodias refers to legends in which she continues to act out her vengeance by piercing the Baptist's tongue or forehead....Lucas reveals the dramatic, psychologically critical moment when Herod fully realizes the appalling consequence of having granted Salomé's wish that John be beheaded.

30. PIETER BRUEGEL, the Elder
Eindhoven about 1525 - 1569 Bruxelles

Landscape with Rabbit Hunters, 1560

Etching
221 x 287 mm.; 8 1/16 x 11 3/8 inches.

Watermark:
Chalice, cf. Briquet nos. 4556-88, dated by Briquet to mid-sixteenth century

References:
Bastelaer 1
Hollstein 1
Lebeer 62

Notes:
1. A very fine impression of this extremely rare etching, the only known original print executed by the hand of Bruegel himself. This impression is well printed, with tone and, unusually, has retained the entire blank title space below the image.
2. This work has been dated 1566 by Lebeer, Bastelaer and Hollstein. However the Institut Néerlandais in Paris (inv. 6959) has a pen and brown ink copy, dated 1560, of the lost Bruegel drawing for this etching. This pen and ink copy is reproduced as cat. no. 75 in : *Bruegel der Ältere als Zeichner*, Lutz Malke, Berlin, 1975. Malke (page 70 of Berlin catalog) thus feels that the date on this etching should be read as 1560 rather than 1566, as had been believed previously. In addition, it would appear that the date of 1560 is stylistically more consistent with Bruegel's drawings of the period such as the small landscapes of 1559-1561 (for examples : Berlin cat. nos. 76-80). Finally this new dating has been confirmed by Timothy A. Riggs (page 172 of : "Bruegel and his Publisher' in *Pieter Bruegel und Seine Welt,* Kunsthistorischen Institut der Freien Universität Berlin and Kupferstichkabinett der Staatlichen Museen Stiftung Preussischer Kulturbesitz, Berlin, 1975).
3. Concerning the rareness of this etching, to our knowledge there are only four impressions in U. S. museums: namely those at the Museum of Fine Arts in Boston, the Metropolitan Museum of Art in New York, the National Gallery of Art in Washington, D.C., as well as the very fine impression acquired in 1966 by the late Harold Joachim for the Art Institute of Chicago. There also have been two additional impressions in a private US collection. Thus, to our present knowledge, together with this present impression, there are only seven impressions of this work in the United States. Hollstein in his catalog notes only three impressions to have come onto the world art markets between 1900 and 1950, namely those of the collections of Peltzer, Schoeller and Friedrich August II. In the thirty-five following years (1950-1985), only a few other impressions, including this one, have come to the fore. In conclusion, this etching undoubtedly is one of the rarest of the great works in the domain of Old Master Prints.

Collection:
Private Collection

31. PIETER BRUEGEL, the Elder (after)
Eindhoven about 1525 - 1569 Bruxelles

Fuga Deiparae in Aegyptum (2nd State), 1553-1557
Flight in Egypt

Etching with engraving by Jan van Doetechum (Deventer 1530 - 1606 Haarlem) and/or Lucas van Doetechum (Deventer active 1544 - about 1580)
315 x 426 mm.; 12 7/16 x 16 inches

Watermark:
Letter with Pillar

References:
Bastelaer 15-II (as "after Bruegel")
Hollstein 13 (as "after Bruegel")

Notes:
A fine impression of the 2nd State of this etching/engraving, with the name "Bruegel" added above the address of H. Cock. In the lower right of this work, the publisher is indicated as Hieronymous Cock. In the past, such engravings often were attributed to the hand of Cock himself who also was a fine printmaker. Most of such works, including this one, now are attributed to the brothers Joannes and/or Lucas van Doetechum who worked for Cock. The "excud. H. Cock" here appears to only signify that Cock was the publisher.Otherwise, on these questions, see: Orenstein (Nadine M. Orenstein, *Pieter Bruegel the Elder: Drawings and Prints,* The Metropolitan Museum of Art, New York, 2001: no. 33, pp. 133-134) as well as: Oberhuber (Konrad Oberhuber *Zwischen Renaissance von Bruegel und Bellange,* Vienna 1967-1968: p. 48).

32. PIETER BRUEGEL, the Elder (after)
Eindhoven about 1525 - 1569 Bruxelles

A Man of War, 1565

Engraving by Frans Huys (1522-1562) after Pieter Bruegel, the Elder, and with possible engraved additions probably by Cornelis Cort (1533/1536 - 1578)
240 x 187 mm.; 9 5/8 x 7 5/8 inches

References:
Bastelaer 98-I/II (as "after Bruegel")
Hollstein 98-I/II

Notes: (as "after Bruegel")
1. A fine impression of the 1st State of this work, with the 1564 inscription "Die Scip".
2. This is one of a series of ten ship scenes executed, it appears, after now lost preparatory drawings by Bruegel. The first eight of these works were engraved by Frans Huys who died in 1562. This work, the ninth of the series, appears to have been initiated by Frans Huys, but then finished by another engraver (probably Cornelis Cort) from the workshop of the Antwerp publisher, Hieronymus Cock. On this question, see: Sellink (Manfred Sellink in: Nadine M. Orenstein *Pieter Bruegel the Elder: Drawings and Prints,* The Metropolitan Museum of Art, New York, 2001: pp. 217-218) and Riggs (Timothy Riggs "Bruegel and His Publisher" in: *Pieter Bruegel und seine Welt,* Otto Georg von Simson and Matthias Winner, eds. Berlin, 1979: p. 173).

FVGA DEIPARAE   IN AEGYPTVM.

33. HANS LAUTENSACK
Bamberg 1524 - about 1560 Vienna

David and Goliath, 1551

Etching on two joined sheets of cream laid paper
170 x 227 mm.; 6 3/4 x 9 inches

Watermark:
Small unidentified watermark

Provenance:
Museum of Fine Arts, Boston (Lugt 282), with its duplicate stamp

Notes:
1. A very fine, well printed impression of this rare work, printed from two plates.
2. The biblical reference here is from the *First Book of Samuel*, XVII:

...The Philistines were stationed on one hill and the Israelites on an opposite hill, with a valley between them...A champion named Goliath of Gath came out from the Philistine camp; he was six and a half feet tall. He had a bronze helmet on his head and wore a bronze corselet of scale armor weighing five thousand shekels, and bronze greaves, and had a bronze scimitar slung from a baldric. The shaft of his javelin was like a weaver's heddle-bar, and its iron head weighed six hundred shekels. He shouted to the ranks of Israel: "Choose one of your own men, and have him come down to me. If he beats me in combat, we will be your vassals; but if I beat him and kill him, you shall be our vassals and serve us." ... Saul and all the men of Israel were dismayed and terror-stricken. Then David spoke to Saul: "Let your majesty not loose courage, I am at your service to go and fight this Philistine". But Saul then said to David: "You cannot go up against this Philistine and fight with him, for you are only a youth, while he has been a warrior from his youth". Then David said to Saul: "Your servant used to tend his father's sheep, and whenever a lion or a bear came to carry off a sheep from the flock, I would go after it and attack it and rescue the prey from its mouth. If it attacked me, I would seize it by the jaw, strike it and kill it...The Lord, who delivered me from the claws of of the lion and the bear, will also keep me safe from the clutches of this Philistine"...The Philistine cursed David by his gods and said to him: "Come here to me and I will leave your flesh for the birds of the air and the beasts of the fields". David answered him: "You come against me with sword and spear and scimitar, but I come against you in the name of the Lord of hosts...Today the Lord will deliver you into my hand".
The Philistine then moved to meet David at close quarters, while David ran quickly toward the battle line in the direction of the Philistine. David put his hand into a bag and took out a stone, hurled it with the sling, and struck the Philistine on the forehead...who thereupon fell prostrate on the ground. Then...with the Philistine's own sword, David dispatched him and cut off his head...

34. JAN VAN LONDERSEEL

Antwerp about 1570 - 1624/25 Rotterdam

Christ and His Disciples at Emmaus, circa 1600-1610

Engraving after David Vinckboons (Malines 1576 - 1629 Amsterdam)
312 x 485 mm.; 12 1/4 x 19 1/8 inches

Watermark:
Eagle in A Circle

Reference:
Hollstein 28

Notes:
1. A fine impression of this beautiful work in which Londerseel has captured the magical atmosphere of Vinckboons' forest scene.
2. Vinckboons himself executed a small number of etchings and engravings after his own works (see: Clifford S. Ackley, *Printmaking the Age of Rembrandt*, Museum of Fine Arts, Boston, 1980: nos 21 and 22, pp. 39-41). In the tradition of Pieter Bruegel, however, Vinckboons also created many drawings made to be engraved or etched by other artists. It appears that the works of Vinckboons were more often reproduced than those of any other artist in the early seventeenth century in northern Netherlands. Engravers and etchers inspired by the works of Vinckboons included Nicholaes de Bruyn, Claes Janz Vischer, Pieter Serwouters and Jan van Londerseel.

35. AEGIDIUS SADELER

Antwerp 1570 - 1629 Prague

Apostrophe ad Venerem
Venus Receiving Gifts

Engraving after Bartholomaeus Spranger (1546-1611)
284 x 190 mm.; 11 3/16 x 7 1/2 inches

Watermark:
Eagle, cf. Briquet 171, Klingenberg (Wurzberg), 1596

Reference:
Hollstein 110 (after Bartholomaeus Spranger)

Notes:
1. A very fine impression of this splendid engraving.
2. Aegidius Sadeler became a member of the Antwerp Engravers Guild in 1589, went to Rome in 1593, to Munich in 1595 and then to Prague where he worked for emperors Rudolph II, Mathias and Ferdinand II. It was in Prague where he began a working relationship with the artist Bartholomaeus Spranger.

APOSTROPHE AD VENEREM.
Primitiis gnata faecunda fertilis anni   Omnia seruitiis obstricta tenentur amoris
Oblatis Dominam te VENVS alma, colunt   Qui vinclum vitæ cuncta creata ligat.
Ancl. Aràkll equo cen.

36. JAN HARMENSZ. MULLER
Amsterdam 1571-1628 Amsterdam

Bellona Leading the Armies of the Emperor Against the Turks (1st State), 1600

Engraving after Bartholomeus Spranger (Antwerp1546-1611 Prague)
515 x 368 mm; 27 3/4 x 20 inches

References:
Bartsch 87
Hollstein 50-I

Notes:
1. A very fine impression of the 1st State (before later publishers' addresses) of this major and extremely rare work, executed on two sheets of copper and then joined at the center of the composition.
2. Jan Harmensz Muller at first followed closely in the footsteps of Hendrik Goltzius for whom he worked until about 1589, but then gradually evolved into Goltzius' chief rival. Most of Muller's engraved works were after either Cornelisz van Haarlem or Bartholomeus Spranger.
3. The subject of this engraving, *Bellona Leading the Armies of Emperor Against the Turks,* had been preceded by another of Muller's major engravings, *The Arts in Flight from the Barbarians* (ref. Bartsch 76, Hollstein 72, the New Hollstein 76). This earlier engraving was already an indictment of the lack of civilization of the Turks who had conquered the Greeks. Muller's *Bellona* and *The Arts in Flight* are among the major prints produced by Netherlandish mannierism. In this present work, Bellona leads not only the Emperor's armies but also civilization itself against the onslaught of the barbarians (see: Larry Silver "Imitation & Emulation: Goltzius as Evolutionary Reproductive Engraver" in *Graven Images*: *The Rise of Professional Printmakers in Antwerp and Haarlem 1540-1640*, Northwestern University, 1993: pages 86 and 87).

(detail also reproduced on cover)

37. JAN VAN DE VELDE II
Rotterdam 1593-1641 Enkhuyzen

The Armed Château

Etching
134 x 198 mm.; 5 1/4 x 7 3/4 inches

Reference:
Hollstein 250 II/III
Franken-van der Kellen 289

Notes:
A fine impression of this beautiful subject.

(not illustrated)

38-41. JAN VAN AKEN
Amsterdam 1614-1661 Amsterdam

Four Views of the Rhine (a set, all 3rd States of Six States)

Four etchings after Hermann Saftleven (Rotterdam about 1609 - 1685 Utrecht)
217 x 277 mm.; 8 9/16 x 10 15/16 inches

Watermark:
Crowned Coat of Arms With Letters JR

References:
38. Hollstein 18-III/VI *Landscape with Peasants on a Hilltop* (illustrated opposite)
39. Hollstein 19-III/VI *Landscape with Man Carrying a Rucksack*
40. Hollstein 20-III/VI *Landscape with Men Catching Crayfish*
41. Hollstein 21-III/VI *Landscape with Resting Travellers*

Notes:
1. Very fine and very rare 3rd State impressions before the addition of the address of the publisher Nicolaus Visscher and before the overall re-working.
2. David Freedberg (*Dutch Landscape Prints,* British Museum, London, 1980) reproduces no. 39 (pl. 126) and also quotes (p. 16) from 17th century Dutch poet Joost van den Vondel's poem based on the sketch books of Hermann Saftleven:

> ...if someone wishes to take the air whenever he likes, but in the peace and quiet of his home, he can still silently go up the Rhine, from Old Utrecht and the Cathedral, between the banks of the rivers, between vineyards, woods and trees; he can enjoy himself amongst the castles, towers and estates, and see cattle, cows, villages and towns; oaks, fields, hedges and fences; springs and waterfalls -all in his own room; he has simply to open these artistic pages, so full of life and grace...

42. ALLAERT VAN EVERDINGEN
Alkmaar 1621-1675 Amsterdam

The Pointed Rock (2nd State)

Etching
106 x 145 mm.; 4 1/4 x 5 3/4 inches

Provenance:
Artaria (Lugt 90). Dealer-collectors in Vienna since 1770.

Reference:
Hollstein 74-II/III

Notes:
A fine impression of the rare 2nd State (of three states).
(not illustrated)

43. REMBRANDT HARMENSZ. VAN RIJN
Leiden 1606 - 1669 Amsterdam

Jan Cornelis Sylvius, Preacher (1st State), 1633

Etching, drypoint and engraving
166 x 142 mm.; 6 5/8 x 5 5/8 inches

Provenance:
Unknown collector (Lugt 824)
Wetterauer Collection, ink stamp on verso (not in Lugt)

Reference:
Bartsch 266
Biörklund/Barnard 33-H
Hollstein (White/Boon) 266

Notes:
1. A superb, brilliant and early 1st State impression with inky plate edges and touches of burr around the eyes and under the left ear. In the following 2nd State, particularly seen in the re-worked contours around the head of Sylvius, much of the harmony and luminosity of the 1st State is lost.
2. This impression is an example of Biörklund's 1st State (of two), Usticke's 1st State (of three) and White/Boon's 1st State (of two).
3. This appears to be the first Rembrandt etched portrait of someone who was not an immediate member of his family. However, Jan Cornelis Sylvius (1564 - 1638), a preacher in the Reform Church of Holland, was indirectly related to Rembrandt in that he married Aeltje Uylenburgh, the sister of the father of Saskia Uylenburgh. Rembrandt married Saskia in 1634, the year after this portrait. Sylvius, established in Amsterdam from 1610 on, had been the tutor of Saskia who as an orphan had arrived in his house in about 1632. It thus was Sylvius who gave his consent to the marriage of Rembrandt and Saskia.
4. The years 1632 and 1633 represented Rembrandt's most intensive activity as a portraitist. Of the fifty or so dated works from those years, forty-six are portraits. The subject of this rather severe but powerful portrait, Jan Cornelis Sylvius, is shown before an open book, presumably a bible. Treated in a baroque manner, with strong contrasts of blacks and whites, Sylvius looks out at us without directly engaging our eyes. As portrayed by Rembrandt, he comes on as a man who accords little importance to the surrounding exterior world.

44. REMBRANDT HARMENSZ. VAN RIJN
Leiden 1606 - 1669 Amsterdam

The Tribute Money (1st State), circa 1635

Etching with drypoint
75 x 103 mm.; 2 3/4 x 4 inches

Provenance:
A.P.F. Robert-Dumesnil (Lugt 2200)
S. William Pelletier (with his mark)

Reference:
Bartsch/Hollstein 68
Hind 124
Biörklund/Barnard 35-2

Notes:
1. A very fine, early impression of the 1st State (of two states), printing with rich burr and with inky plate edges.
2. According to the *Bible* (Matthew XXII, 15-22), the Pharisees understood the growing influence of Jesus who had chased the money-changers from the temple and who had become known for apparently having healed the blind, the lame and other afflicted ones. They therefore tried to entrap Jesus concerning a question of a point of law:

   > "Tell us then...is it lawful to pay a census tax to Caesar or not?"...[Jesus replied]: "Show me the coin that pays the census tax.". They then handed him a Roman coin. He thereupon said to them: "Whose image is this and whose inscription?". They replied: "Caesar's". He then said to them: "Then repay to Caesar what belongs to Caesar and to God what belongs to God". When they heard this...they went away.

3. In this etching, Rembrandt has very carefully adhered to the biblical text. The subject clearly is a sequence to his *Christ Driving the Money-Changers from the Temple*. Both of these works date from the same year of 1635, but, in their ordering, Bartsch/Hollstein date *The Tribute Money* as having been etched slightly earlier during that year.
4. The provenance on this work includes Alexandre-Pierre-François Robert-Dumesnil (Paris 1778 - 1864 Paris). Robert-Dumesnil was the author of the eight volumes: *Peintre-Graveur Français*. His interest in collecting prints started n 1826 and took over his life by 1835 when he abandoned his business activities in order to devote himself entirely to the world of print collecting. His idea , in developing his books on printmaking, was to add to the earlier accomplishments of Bartsch (Adam Bartsch, *Le Peintre Graveur,* 21 vols., Vienna, 1802-1821). The title of his first volume was: *Peintre-Graveur Français, ou catalogue raisonné des estampes gravées par les peintres et les dessinateurs de l'école Française, ouvrage faisant suite au "Peintre-Graveur" de M. Bartsch.* The first six volumes of Robert-Dumesnil appeared by 1850. The last two volumes were completed later by Georges Duplessis, curator at the Bibliothèque Nationale.

45. REMBRANDT HARMENSZ. VAN RIJN
Leiden 1606 - 1669 Amsterdam

Christ Driving the Money Changers from the Temple, 1635

Etching
140 x 167 mm.; 5 1/2 x 6 5/8 inches

Provenance:
S. William Pelletier (with his mark)

Reference:
Bartsch/Hollstein 69
Hind 126
Biörklund/Barnard 35-B

Notes:
1. A very strong, well-printed and early impression. Nowell-Usticke's 1st State (of seven states).
2. Followed closely by Rembrandt, the biblical reference here is *Mark* 12, 15:

> ...They came to Jerusalem, and on entering the temple area, he [Jesus] began to drive o u t those selling and buying there. He overturned the tables of the money-changers and the seats of those who were selling doves. He did not allow anyone to carry anything through the temple area. Then he informed them, saying:
>
> My house shall be called a house of prayer for all peoples. But you have made it a den of thieves...

3. The former owner of this work, the late S. William Pelletier, was one of the most astute 20th century collectors of 17th century Dutch prints. Together with Leonard J. Slatkes and Linda Stone-Ferrier, Pelletier was the author of *Adriaen Van Ostade: Etchings of Peasant Life in Holland's Golden Age* (edited by Patricia Phagan), Georgia Museum of Art, University of Georgia, 1993.

46. REMBRANDT HARMENSZ. VAN RIJN

Leiden 1606-1669 Amsterdam

The Great Jewish Bride, 1635

Etching with some drypoint and burin
222 x 168 mm.; 8 3/4 x 6 5/8 inches

Provenance:
1. Baron Hans Albrecht von Derschau (ref. Lugt 2510), who died in 1824 was from Nürnberg and was well-known for his publications from 1808 to 1816 on the history of the woodcut, *Holzschnitte alter Deutscher Meister in den Original Platten.* Already in 1780, von Derschau had acquired hundreds of woodcuts which originally had come from the collection of Dürer's friend Willibald Pirkheimer. Von Derschau also acquired many works from the famous collection of Johann Gustav Silberrad (died 1782). Von Derschau sold a considerable collection of prints to the King of Prussia in 1817. These latter works (including this present Rembrandt) then came into the hands of the Kupferstichkabinett (Print Collection) of the National Museum in Berlin around 1831.
2. Kupferstichkabinett des Staatlichen Museen, Berlin (ref. Lugt 1606 and 2398), 1831. The Berlin Kupferstichkabinett was based on the acquisition of only four collections: that of the Baron von Derschau; that of King Friedrich Wilhelm I (1713-1740); those of the ensemble of the collections of the Count of Lepell, the Count of Cornellian and a Prof. Weitsch; and finally that of the "Generalpostmeister" K.F.F. von Nagler. This present Rembrandt was sold as a duplicate, probably in 1871.
3. C. and R. Hirschler (Lugt 633a). According to Lugt (Frits Lugt *Les Marques de Collections, Supplément*, La Hague, 1956: p. 91), Carl Hirschler (1871-1941) and his wife Rose went to Haarlem where he became director of the Bunge Co. of Amsterdam. Their print collection consisted principally of works by Schongauer, van Meckenem, Dürer and Rembrandt as well as the complete etched works of van Ostade and Bega.

References:
Bartsch/Hollstein 340-V/V
Hind 127
Biörklund/Barnard 35-C

Notes:
1. A fine impression of this major work.
2. White/Boon indicate various possible identifications for this subject. Valentiner suggested an actress on a stage (Minerva?). Weisbach and Benesch suggested a Sibyl. On the other hand, M. Kahr *(Oud Holland,* 1966 (lxxxi), p.244 ff.) suggested that the subject was Esther holding the decree and meditating over the slaying of the Jews. White-Boon refer to Landsberger's study *Rembrandt, the Jews and the Bible*, Philadelphia, 1946, p. 74, where it has been pointed out that a Jewish bride received her husband with her hair down and the Ketubah in her hand. The traditional title, however, derives from the supposition that the sitter was the daughter of Ephraim Bonus the subject of another of Rembrandt's famous etchings: *Ephraim Bonus, Jewish Physician*, 1647 (ref. Bartsch, 278).

Collection:
Private Collection, Oak Brook

47. REMBRANDT HARMENSZ. VAN RIJN
Leiden 1606 - 1669 Amsterdam

Joseph Telling His Dreams (2nd State), 1638

Etching
111 x 84 mm.; 4 1/4 x 3 1/4 inches

Provenance:
J. Camesina de Pomal (Lugt 429)
A. Artaria (Lugt 33)
Biörklund (Lugt 1138c)
S. William Pelletier (with his mark)

Reference:
Bartsch/Hollstein 37
Hind 160
Biörklund/Barnard 38-E

Notes:
1.   A very fine, early impression of the 2nd State (of three states), with burr lower left and on the spine of the book.
2.   The biblical reference here is from *Genesis* XXXVII, 1-11, in which Joseph tells his brothers of his dreams:

> ...Listen to this dream I had. There we were, binding sheaves in the field, when suddenly my sheath rose to an upright position, and your sheaves formed a ring around my sheave and bowed down to it...I had another dream...this time, the sun and the moon and eleven stars were bowing down to me...Exasperated with Joseph's "dreams", Joseph's brothers eventually sold him to the Ishmaelites.

3.   The collector's mark on this work of Josef Camesina de Pomal (1765-1827) is of particular interest. Camesina de Pomal was from Vienna, was a major collector of prints and drawings and appears to have been the father of the Viennese historian Albert Ritter von Camesina. After his death in 1827, Camesina de Pomal's extensive collection was sold in Vienna by the dealers Artaria (whose collector's mark is also found on this work) in a series of four auctions between 1831 and 1833. In his description, Lugt (Frits Lugt *Marques de Collections : Dessins-Estampe* Amsterdam, 1922) makes special mention of Camesina de Pomal's Rembrandt etchings (including the present one) which were offered in Artaria's auctions of October, 1832 and April, 1833.

48. REMBRANDT HARMENSZ. VAN RIJN
Leiden 1606-1669 Amsterdam

Man at a Desk Wearing a Cross and Chain (3rd State), 1641

Etching with drypoint
155 x 103 mm.; 6 1/8 x 4 inches

Provenance:
W. E. Drugulin (Lugt 2612)
J. B. E. Gallice (Lugt 1063)
Unidentified collector's stamp (Lugt 796)
G. W. Nowell-Usticke (Parke-Bernet Galleries, New York, Nov. 1st 1967: no. 140)

References:
Bartsch 261-III/IV
Hind 189
Biörklund/Barnard 41-L

Notes:
1. A very fine, rare, early impression, with excellent contrasts, of Bartsch/Hollstein's 3rd State (of four states).
2. From the provenance on this work, there is the mark of Wilhelm Eduard Drugulin (1825-1879) who was a print and drawings dealer, but also was one of the most astute, private, German collectors of the nineteenth century. His collection of portrait prints was acquired by the Rijksmuseum, while his collection of ornamental prints was acquired by the Museum of Industry in Vienna in 1863. Drugulin's most beautiful prints were brought together towards the end of his life when he was able to concentrate his undivided attention to augmenting and refining his private collection. This latter collection, including this work, was sold by auction in 1879, just after the death of Drugulin. A second collector's mark on this work is that of J. B. E. Gallice (1856-1872) who was a major collector of old master prints and drawings, but whose mark only appeared on his prints. Another former owner of this work was Gordon W. Nowell-Usticke, the author of the often-cited: *Rembrandt's Etching States and Values,* Narberth, 1967.

49. REMBRANDT HARMENSZ. VAN RIJN
Leiden 1606 - 1669 Amsterdam

The Circumcision in the Stable (1st State), 1654

Etching
95 x 145 mm.; 3 3/4 x 5 3/4 inches

Reference:
Bartsch 47
White/Boon (Hollstein) 47-I (from II)
Nowell-Usticke 47-I (from III)
Biörklund/Barnard 54-B

Notes:
1. A fine, early impression of White/Boon's 1st State before Rembrandt filled in the blank area, upper-center.
2. The iconographic tradition, as seen for example in Albrecht Dürer's woodcut *Circumcision in the Temple* from the *Life of the Virgin* series, is that this event takes place in the temple. The Bible, however, is not precise concerning the place of the circumcision (Luke II, 21):

> After eight days were completed before his circumcision could take place, he was
> named Jesus, the name given by the angel before he was conceived in the womb.

The normal presentation of Jesus in the temple depicts the parents of Jesus as devout Jews, the faithful observers of the Law of the Lord, that is to say the Law of Moses. Rembrandt, in his earliest depiction of this scene (Bartsch 48, circa 1630), also placed this scene in the temple. However, as might have been pointed out to Rembrandt at that time, the Law of Moses does not allow young mothers to enter the temple until after a "purification" period of forty days. Thus, in order to include Mary in the scene, Rembrandt here reverts to the same manger location as in the *Nativity*. In addition, the warmth and simplicity of the manger corresponded more truly to the sensitivity of Rembrandt's feelings than the hieratic grandiosity of the Temple. In 1661, representing this scene in a painting some seven years later (National Gallery of Art, Washington, D.C.), Rembrandt repeated his choice of the manger for the depiction of the circumcision.

50. REMBRANDT HARMENSZ. VAN RIJN

Leiden 1606 - 1669 Amsterdam

The Descent from the Cross by Torchlight, 1654

Etching with drypoint
205 x 161 mm. (sheet: 218 x 169 mm.); 8 x 6 3/8 inches (sheet: 8 1/2 x 6 5/8 in.)

Reference:
Bartsch/Hollstein 83
Hind 280
Biörklund/Barnard 54-G

Notes:

1. A superb, early impression with rich burr on the figure pulling down the sheet and on the figure supporting Christ's body and elsewhere.

2. This scene relates to the description of *Matthew* (XXVII, 57-59):

> When it was evening, there came a rich man from Arimathea named Joseph who was himself a disciple of Jesus. He went to Pilate and asked for the body of Jesus; then Pilate ordered it to be handed over. Taking the body, Joseph wrapped it in clean linen and laid it in his new tomb that he had hewn in the rock. Then he rolled a huge stone across the entrance to the tomb and departed. But Mary Magdalene and the other Mary remained sitting there, facing the tomb...

3. Rembrandt, in his interpretation of this scene, has infused it with that emotional intensity characteristic of his later etchings. The contents of this scene are transmitted not only with the pictoral elements involved, but also with the broad and powerful etched lines as well as with the dramatic profundity of the shadows created with drypoint. Within the deep shadows of the night as well as with the hopelessness of the situation, Rembrandt's emotion is not expressed with his figures as much as it is expressed with the luminosity in which this lamp-lit scene is entrenched.

(also illustrated on page 6)

51. REMBRANDT HARMENSZ. VAN RIJN
Leiden 1606 - 1669 Amsterdam

Abraham's Sacrifice, 1655

Etching and drypoint
157 x 133 mm.; 6 1/4 x 5 1/4 inches

Watermark:
Strasburg Lily

Provenance:
S. William Pelletier (with his mark)

Reference:
Bartsch/Hollstein 35
Hind 283
Biörklund/Barnard 55-B

Notes:
1. A superb, early impression with inky plate edges and printing with considerable plate-tone. Strong burr on Abraham's shirt and also on the left edge of the composition.
2. The reference here is to *Genesis* XXII, 10-12:

> ...God put Abraham to the test. ..Take your son Isaac, your only one, whom you love, and go to the land of Moriah. There you shall offer him up as a holocaust on a height that I will point out to you...On the third day, Abraham got sight of the place from afar. Then he said to his servants: Both of you stay here with the donkey, while the boy and I go on over yonder...When they came to the place of which God had told him, Abraham built an altar and arranged the wood on it. Next he tied up his son Isaac and put him on top of the wood of the altar. Then he reached out and took out the knife to slaughter his son. But the Lord's messenger called out to him from heaven: "Abraham, Abraham...Do not lay your hand on the boy...I know now how devoted you are to God, since you did not withhold from me your own beloved son. ..As Abraham looked about, he spied a ram caught by its horns in the thicket. So he went and took the ram and offered it up as a holocaust in place of his son.

3. Instead of representing the Angel "calling from heaven", as descibed in *Genesis,* Rembrandt brings the Angel, with fluttering wings and hair still agitated from the wind of the flight, directly onto the scene. The angel has vigorously seized the arms of Abraham, stopping him physically from carrying out the barbaric sacrifice which he thought had been assigned to him by God. This work again shows to what extent Rembrandt read and studied the Bible. In this case, all the elements of this scene, as described in the Bible, are present: the angel, the two servants, the donkey, and even the ram. To all of these, Rembrandt added one previously undescribed element: the sacrificial altar.
4. The former owner of this work, the late S. William Pelletier, was one of the most astute 20th century collectors of 17th century Dutch prints. Together with Leonard J. Slatkes and Linda Stone-Ferrier, Pelletier was the author of *Adriaen Van Ostade: Etchings of Peasant Life in Holland's Golden Age* (edited by Patricia Phagan), Georgia Museum of Art, University of Georgia, 1993.

52. REMBRANDT HARMENSZ. VAN RIJN
Leiden 1606 - 1669 Leiden

The Flight into Egypt: Crossing a Brook, 1654

Etching
97 x 145 mm.; 3 3/4 x 5 3/4 inches

Reference:
Bartsch/Hollstein 55
Hind 276
Biörklund/Barnard 54-D

Notes:
1. A fine, early impression of the only state of this intimately conceived work. With touches of burr and the scratch across the Virgin's cheek visible, all corresponding to an early impression.
2. The biblical scene here takes place just after *The Visit of the Magi* (Matthew 2:1-12). Except for the addition of the "brook", in his etching, Rembrandt closely follows the text of Matthew 2: 13-15:

> When they [the Magi] had departed, behold, the angel of the Lord appeared to Joseph in a dream and said: "Rise, take the child and his mother, flee to Egypt, and stay there until I tell you. Herod is going to search for the child to destroy him". Joseph rose and took the child and his mother by night and departed for Egypt.

54. CORNELIS DUSART
Haarlem 1660 - 1704 Haarlem

Violinist in a Tavern, about 1685

Etching
280 x 247 mm.; 11 x 9 3/4 inches

Watermark:
Arms of Amsterdam

Provenance:
Count Giuseppe Archinto (Lugt 546)
Langdon-Dorn Collection (not in Lugt)

Reference:
Bartsch 15
Hollstein 15 III

Notes:
1. A very fine, light-filled and richly printed impression of one of Dusart's major etchings.
2. Dusart was a pupil of Adriaen van Ostade (1610 - 1685) and inherited much of the contents of Van Ostade's studio. His style derives partially from that of Ostade, but also from that of another Dutch artist of the times, Jan Steen (1626 - 1679). Dusart painted scenes of seventeenth-century, Dutch peasant life. In addition to fourteen or fifteen etchings, he also executed a number of aquatints. Most, if not all, of his etchings were executed around 1685.
3. The provenance of this work includes the famous early nineteenth-century collector, Count Giuseppe Archinto (1783 - 1861) from Milano. Lugt (Frits Lugt *Marques de Collections:Dessins et Estampes*, Amsterdam, 1921) has written a considerable description of this collector:

> Count Giuseppe Archinto belonged to an old and established family in which there were art collectors starting already at the end of the seventeenth century. His collection, which was more or less conserved and administered by the print dealer Giuseppe Vallardi, was dispersed after the death of Archinto in Paris... first his paintings on May 18, 1863 and later his prints. This latter sale, however, did not give a true idea of the vast variety of prints covered by the collection. The collection included magnificent works by Dürer, Rembrandt, Van Dyck and other great painter-engravers...

Rusticus ex animo, non pullus Hijpocrita, gaudet.

55. ADRIAEN VAN DE VELDE
Amsterdam 1636-1672 Amsterdam

Horses and Cattle in a Wooded Landscape, about 1663

Pen, brown ink and gray wash, with mark of J. de Vos on verso
150 x 200 mm.; 5 15/16 x 7 15/16 inches

Provenance:
J. Goll van Franchenstein, no. 15
Vente Mensing, April 27-29, 1937: no. 741, where acquired by a M. Hirschmann.
A private Belgian collector

Notes:
1. One of two known studies for a painting of 1663 in the Mauritshuis, The Hague (no. 197 and Hofstede de Groot no. 140). The other was in the collection of Emile Wolf, New York (see: Herbert F. Johnson Museum of Art, Ithaca, New York *Dutch Drawings of the Seventeenth Century from a Collection,* 1979, no 50. Also see: W.R. Robinson *Master Drawings,* 1979, XVII, p. 19, no. B3). Robinson (ref. above) notes that practically all of Van de Velde's known preparatory drawings for paintings fall in the last decade of the artist's brief career. With respect to Van de Velde's working methods, it appeared that he went into the fields at least once a week in order to sketch horses and cattle in landscapes. On this, see: Arnold Houbraken *De Groote Schouburgh d Nederlantsche Konstchilders en Schilderessen...,* III, Amsterdam, 1721, p.90 (also cited by Robinson, note 12, ref. above).
2. Differing slightly from our description, Jan Filedt de Kok dates this wash-drawing by Adriaen van de Velde as just after, rather than just before the 1663 painting in the Mauritshuis.

III
Eighteenth Century
Prints and Drawings

56. HENDRIK TAVENIER
Haarlem 1734 - 1807 Haarlem

Landscape with Castle, 1779

Watercolor
263 x 341 mm.; 10 3/8 x 13 1/2 inches
Signed and dated on verso in brown ink: *H. Tavenier, 1779*

Notes:
1. Hendrik Tavenier executed many idyllic views of the ruins of castles and monasteries as they appeared in eighteenth-century Holland. This watercolor, dating from 1779, is a typical and beautiful example.
2. Tavenier, born fourteen years after G. B. Piranesi (1720 -1778), considered the ruins of antiquity very differently than his predecessor. Piranesi's interest was that of an artist, but also those of an archaeologist and of an architect. He was interested as much in the inner construction of the monuments of antiquity as in their exterior appearance. Following the prettified ruin-landscapes created by Hubert Robert (1733 - 1808) and in the immediate suite of Piranesi, Tavenier made use of the ruins of antiquity simply as romantic and beautiful settings for his depictions of everyday, eighteenth-century Dutch life.

57. JEAN-ANTOINE WATTEAU (after)
Valenciennes 1684 - 1721 Nogent-sur-Marne

Fêtes Vénitiennes (1st State in pure etching), 1732
Venetian Celebrations

Pure etching, before all additional engraving, by Laurent Cars (Lyon 1699 - 1771 Paris)
463 x 368 mm.; 18 1/4 x 14 1/2 inches

Reference:
Dacier and Vuaflart 6-I/VI

Notes:
1. An extremely rare impression in pure etching only of the 1st State (of 6 states). As to the importance of such early proofs in pure etching before the addition of engraving and referring to the pure etching proofs of Charles-Nicholas Cochin Père (1668-1754), J. M. Fisher writes (*Regency to Empire: French Printmaking 1715-1814,* Victor I. Carlson and John W. Ittmann, The Baltimore Museum of Art and The Minneapolis Institute of Arts 1984: pp. 77, 79): "...Such proofs, which were highly valued by nineteenth century collectors like the Goncourts, must be regarded as unfinished preparatory states. Collectors and writers in the nineteenth century, anxious to find a precedent for etching as a free and spontaneous technique, embraced such proofs as evidence of an unexpected freedom in the eighteenth century"...
2. Laurent Cars (1699-1771) is one of the most highly considered of the French eighteenth century interpretative printmakers and *Fêtes Vénitiennes* is one of his most well known accomplishments.
3. This work was etched and engraved after one of Watteau's most beautiful paintings, a painting first offered by the widow of F. Chereau and Surugue in the *Mercure* of July 1732 (p.1609). The painting was one of the eight Watteaus in the collection of Watteau's dealer Jean de Jullienne when he died. With respect to this particular painting, Dacier & Vuaflart refer to a study published by Eugène Bouvy in *Etudes Italiennes* (April-June 1921, p. 65 and following) questioning whether Watteau had been inspired by Danchet's famous ballet with music by Campra: *Les Fêtes Vénitiennes,* given for the first time at the Paris Opera on June 17, 1710.

58. NICOLAS LANCRET (after)
Paris 1690 - 1743 Paris

Musique à la Campagne (undescribed 1st State in pure etching)
Music in the Countryside

Etching by Etienne Fessard (Paris 1714 - 1777 Paris)
362 x 265 mm.; 14 1/4 x 10 1/2 inches

Reference:
Portalis and Beraldi 12

Notes:
A fine impression in an undescribed, perhaps unique 1st State in pure etching only. Small margins except where trimmed into the blank area below.

(illustrated on page 118)

59. JEAN-FRANÇOIS JANINET
Paris 1752-1814 Paris

Portrait of Marie Antoinette (2nd State), 1777
After Jean-Baptiste-André Gautier-Dagoty (about 1740-about 1786)

Etching and engraving printed on two sheets as follows: oval portrait on full sheet in yellow, blue, red and black inks from four plates; decorative frame, cut in center, printed in blue and orange inks from two plates.
255 x 205 mm.; 10 x 7 in., oval image
408 x 319 mm.; 16 x 12 1/2 inches, printed border

Inscriptions:
Below oval portrait, masked by frame:
Gravé par Janinet en 1777./Marie-Antoinette d'Autriche/Reine de France et de Navarre/Née à Vienne le 2.9bre 1755./Mariée à Versailles le 16. de May 1770./Imprimé par Blin
Below oval frame, flanking central coat-of-arms:
MARIE-ANTte D'AUTRICHE/Reine de France – et de Navarre

Reference:
Inventaire 18e siècle 12:29, no. 56.
Regency to Empire : French Printmaking 1715-1814, Victor I. Carlson and John W. Ittmann, The Baltimore Museum of Art and The Minneapolis Institute of Arts, 1985: see no. 66 (a 3rd state), ill. on p. 205.

Notes:
1. A very fine impression with pristine colors of the 2nd State (of three states) of this exceedingly rare and complex plate, one of the master prints produced in late eighteenth-century France. In the 3rd State, there are flecks of gold added to the orange-gold colored flowers and ornamentation of the oval frame.
2. John Ittmann (reference above, p. 204) notes the similar 2nd State impression of this work at the Art Institute of Chicago.

MARIE·ANT.ᵗᵉ   D'AUTRICHE,
Reine de France   et de Navarre.

99

60. LOUIS-LEOPOLDE BOILLY
La Bassée 1761-1845 Paris

Payez, passez or *L'Averse*, about 1800-1805
Pay [in order to] Cross Over or Rain Storm

Pen, wash drawing and gouache
320 x 400 mm.; 12 5/8 x 15 3/4 inches
Below to the left, the stamp of the collection Georges Dormeuil (Lugt 1146a).

Exhibited:
1. *L.L. Boilly*, Galerie J. Seligman et Fils, Paris, June, 1930, no. 103 (exhibit presented by the *Société des Amis du Musée Carnavalet*, lent by Georges Dormeuil).
2. *Exposition d'Art Français*, London, 1932 under title of *Passez, payez, ou L'Averse*.
3. *Chefs-d'oeuvre de l'Art Français*, no. 177 of catalogue.

Provenances:
1. Vente Goncourt, Feb. 17, 1897 where bought by Monsieur Stettiner for 2.100 francs (information provided by Marianne Delafond, Curator at the Musée Marmottan, letter of Feb. 12, 1985).
2. Georges Dormeuil (Lugt 1146a), stamp below to left
3. *Dessins Anciens*, Ader-Picard-Tajan, Palais Galliera, Paris, June 13, 1978: no. 2.

Notes:
1. This watercolor corresponds to the painting of the same subject, belonging to the Louvre in Paris (oil on canvas, 325 x 405 mm). This painting was exhibited as No. 20 in: *Louis Boilly*, Musée Marmotton, Paris, May-June 1984. There also is a crayon drawing with white heightening (370 x 270 mm.) belonging to the Musée Marmotton (Inv. 384) and no. 76 in the 1984 Boilly exhibition at the museum. This latter drawing, showing only a sketch of the three figures to the right in the composition, also was in the 1930 Boilly exhibition (*Société des Amis du Musée Carnavalet*, cat. no. 115). In the Musée Marmotton description of this other preparatory drawing (entitled *L'Averse* c.1805), the catalogue refers to this present watercolor ("dessin rehauseé d'aquarelle et d'encre de Chine...sous le titre *La Passerelle*", 320 x 400 mm.) as the watercolor in the *Vente Goncourt*, Feb. 17, 1897.
2. Georges Dormeuil (1856-1939), the owner of this work until his death in 1939, was one of the most reputed French collectors of recent times. He started his collecting in about 1890 and actively continued until about 1922. His collection extended from the *Haute Époque* to the early nineteeenth century. In 1934, Dormeuil made a major donation to the Louvre of Limoges enamels and other works from the 13th and 14th centuries. Also in 1934, Dormeuil presented the Musée Carnavalet in Paris with a group of works by Gabriel de Saint-Aubin. The strongest element of Dormeuil's collection consisted of paintings and particularly drawings of the 18th Century. The artists represented included Watteau, Fragonard, Gabriel de Saint-Aubin, Hubert Robert, Moreau le Jeune, Boucher, Grueze, Lavreince, Huet, the Cochins, Portail, Lancret, Carmontelle, Leprince, Louis Moreau, Hoin, Mallet, Quentin de La Tour, Perronneau and Boilly.
3. At a time when Jacques-Louis David was turning political events into "historical" paintings, Boilly described more modest occurrences and genre scenes. He diverged considerably from the academic norms of his time and his painting showed a certain Realism which, in subtle ways, was sometimes quite avant-garde. This is one of the reasons for the recent renewal of interest in Boilly.

Collection:
A private collection

61. GIOVANNI BATTISTA PIRANESI
Mogliano 1720 - 1778 Rome

Spaccato interno della Basilica di S. Paolo fuori delle Mura (1st State), 1749
St. Paolo fuori le Mura: Interior

Etching
410 x 605 mm.; 16 1/8 x 23 3/4 inches

Reference:
Hind 7-I/VII

Notes:
An extremely rare impression of the 1st State (of seven states) before the addition, in the 2nd State, of the address of Piranesi's early representatives Bouchard and Gravier. In such very early Piranesi impressions, there is a unique silvery quality which is no longer present in later impressions. The reason for this is that as Piranesi printed his plates, the artist saw those plates weakening. To compensate for this weakening, the plates were more heavily inked and more strongly printed. This resulted in a gradual loss of details and a diminishing of subtlety found in the rare, earliest impressions such as this one.

62. GIOVANNI BATTISTA PIRANESI
Mogliano 1720 - 1778 Rome

Veduta del Ponte Molle sur Tevere due miglia lontan da Roma (1st State), 1762
The Ponte Molle

Etching
444 x 680 mm.; 17 1/8 x 26 3/8 inches

Reference:
Hind 64-I/IV

Notes:
1. A very rare work as a life-time impression. Impressions of the following 2nd State, with the price erased, are already posthumous.
2. The actual translation of Piranesi's text: *Veduta del Ponte Molle sur Tevere due miglia lontan da Roma* would be: "View of the Molle Bridge over the Tiber, Two Miles from Rome". In his catalogue, Hind (Arthur M. Hind *Giovanni Battista Piranesi : A Critical Study*, 1978 edition, The Holland Press Ltd., London: no. 64, p.57) has shortened Piranesi's title to: *The Ponte Molle.*

Spaccato interno della Basilica di S. Paolo fuori delle Mura, eretta da Costantino Magno, divisa in cinque Navate co'sua Crociata. Ottanta Colonne di marmo greco venato di vario colore, quivi trasportate dal Sepolcro di Adriano Imperatore, sostentano le Navate variando di grandezza, e lavoro le laterali da quelle della Navata di mezzo. Altre Colonne dieci di Granito sono quivi per la Crociata; intorno alla quale, come ancora intorno la Navata di mezzo ordinatamente disposti si veggono li Ritratti di tutti i Sommi Pontefici Romani con altre Pitture antiche già quasi consumate dal tempo. Il Pavimento delle Navate è formato di rotti pezzi di marmo, levati dalle Rovine di altri Edificii antichi. *Piranesi f.*

Veduta del Ponte Molle sul Tevere due miglia lontan da Roma. A Ristauri del Pontefice Niccolo V. B Rovine del Ponte supplite con due ponti levatoj. C Torre fabbricata ne' tempi bassi per custodia del Ponte.

63. GIOVANNI BATTISTA PIRANESI
Mogliano 1720 - 1778 Rome

Veduta del Castello dell'Aqua Felice (2nd State), 1751
The Fontana dell'Acqua Felice

Etching
402 x 682 mm.; 15 7/8 x 26 7/8 inches

Reference:
Hind 20-II/V

Notes:
A fine, early 2nd State impression, with the address of the artist and the price still present in the plate.

64. GIOVANNI BATTISTA PIRANESI
Mogliano 1720 - 1778 Rome

Veduta della Curia Ostilia, (3rd State), 1757
The Temple of Claudius at the Church of SS. Giovanni and Paolo

Etching
400 x 603 mm.; 15 3/4 x 23 3/4 inches

Reference:
Hind 43-III/VI

Notes:
1. A fine impression of the 3rd State including the address of the artist, no longer found in the following 4th State.
2. There is a considerable difference between the title of this work, as indicated by Piranesi in the plate and as indicated by Hind in his *catalogue raisonné* of Piranesi's prints. Hind's full title in English is: *Substructure of the Temple of Claudius at the Church of SS. Giovanni E Paolo* (formerly called the *Curia Hostilia*). The difference of titles would appear to be caused by a more recent name given to the same structure.

Veduta del Castello dell'Acqua Felice
presso le Terme Diocleziane. 1 Chiesa di S. Maria della Vittoria

VEDUTA DEL PIANO SUPERIORE DEL SERRAGLIO DELLE FIERE FABBRICATO DA DOMIZIANO A USO DELL'ANFITEATRO FLAVIO, E VOLGARMENTE DETTO LA CURIA OSTILIA.

65. GIOVANNI BATTISTA PIRANESI
Mogliano 1720 - 1778 Rome

Veduta dell'Anfiteatro Flavio, detto il Colosseo (1st State), 1757
The Colosseum

Etching
444 x 701 mm.; 17 1/2 x 27 1/2 inches

Reference:
Hind 57-I/IV

Notes:
The very rare, early 1st State of this work is one of the most sought-after etchings by Piranesi. In the second and following states, the price has been eliminated and impressions are invariably posthumous. Piranesi's title for this work: *Veduta dell'Anfiteatro Flavio, detto Colosseo* (View of the Amphitheater Flavio, called the Colosseum) has been shortened by Hind to: "The Colosseum".

A. *Archi del primi Ordine dell'Anfiteatro, pe' quali il popolo ascendeva ai gradi degli Spettatori.*
B. *Nicina moderna.* C. *Camerini incau nepli stessi archi forse per segno di chi desiderava d'aver rincontra fra la moltitudine degli Spettatori.* D. *Arco senza numero, sopra cui era immaginato il ponte che dalla fabbrica Cesarea sull'Esquilino dava l'ingresso nell'Anfit.* E. *Parte dell'Anfit. dirupata dagl'Incendi.*

Veduta dell'Anfiteatro Flavio, detto il Colosseo

Presso l'Autore a Strada Felice vicino alla Trinità de' Monti.   A paoli due e mezzo.

F. *Archi del secondo e terz'ordine anticamente intrachiusi dà parapetti, de' quali ri-restano alcuni segni e vestibii.* G. *Muraglia su cui poggiavano le antenne di metallo, che passando per la cornice sostenevano la pretenda.* H. *dichiarare intorrento delle antenne, nelle quali era impressa la parte intorrento del medesimo.* I. *Radici del monte Esquilino.* K. *Arco di Costantino.* L. *Monte Celio.* M. *Principio della via di S. Gio. Laterano.*
Piranesi. f.

66. GIOVANNI BATTISTA PIRANESI
Mogliano 1720 - 1778 Rome

Veduta del Tempio d'Antonio e Faustina in Campo Vaccino (3rd State), 1758
The Temple of Antonio and Faustina

Etching
403 x 537 mm.; 15 3/4 x 21 1/4 inches

Reference:
Hind 49-III/VI

Notes:
A fine, early impression of the 3rd State, with the address of the artist and the price.

67. GIOVANNI BATTISTA PIRANESI
Mogliano 1720 - 1778 Rome

Veduta interna dell' Atrio del Portico di Ottavia (3rd State), 1760
The Portico of Octavia: The Entrance Porch, Interior

Etching
410 x 550 mm.; 16 1/8 x 21 5/8 inches

Reference:
Hind 59-III/VI

Note:
The 1st State of this work is before any address, while the 2nd State has the address of Bouchard and Gravier. In this following 3rd State, the address of Piranesi's dealers, Bouchard and Gravier, is replaced by that of Piranesi himself. The following 4th State, in which Piranesi's own address is erased, invariably is posthumous.

Piranesi Architetto fec.

Veduta del Tempio di Antonino e Faustina in Campo Vaccino.   1. S. Lorenzo in Miranda de'Speziali

Presso l'Autore a Strada Felice n.4 Palazzo Tomati vicino alla Trinità de'monti. A paoli due e mezzo.

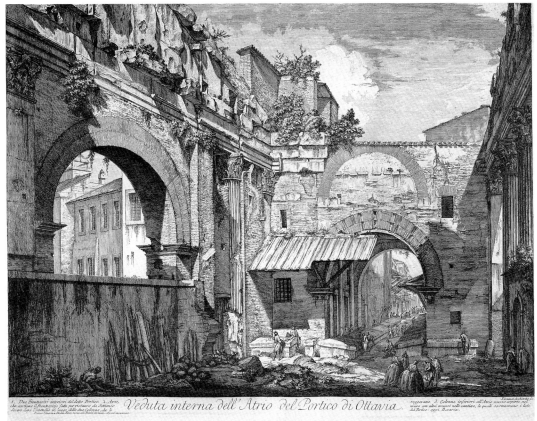

1. Due Frontespizii interiori del detto Portico. 2. Arco,   Veduta interna dell'Atrio del Portico di Ottavia   reggevano. 3. Colonne inferiori all'Atrio mezzo coperte nel
che sostiene il Frontespizio fatto per restauro da Settimio   muro con altri avanzi nelle cantine, le quali sostenevano i lati
Severo Sopr.i l'avanzo in luogo delle due Colonne che la   del Portico: oggi Pescaria.

109

68. FRANCISCO JOSE de GOYA y LUCIENTES
Fuendetodos 1746 - 1828 Bordeaux

Margarita de Austria (1st edition), 1778

Etching on heavy cream laid paper: after Diego Velasquez (1599-1660)
375 x 313 mm.; 14 3/4 x 12 3/8 inches

Reference:
Delteil 7
Harris 6-III/1

Notes:
1. A very fine, well contrasted impression on laid paper of the rare 1st edition of 1778.
2. Goya's full title of this work is: *D. Margarita de Austria, Reyña de España, Muger de Phelipe III/ Pintura de D. Diego Velasquez del tamaño del natural en el Real Palacio de Madrid, dibujada y grabada por D. Fran. Goya Pintor, año de 1778* (Margarita of Austria, Queen of Spain, Wife of Philipe III, Painting by D. Diego Velasquez, of life-size and found in The Royal Palace in Madrid, drawn and etched by D. Fran. Goya, Painter, in the year 1778).
3. Margarita of Austria was born in 1584. Her father was Karl von Steyer, the son of Ferdinand I, while her mother was Maria Anna of Bavaria. In 1599 at the age of 15 years, Margarita married Philip III, eventual King of Spain. She had eight children with Philip III: Philip IV of Spain , Carlos (1607-1632), Fernando (1609-1641), Alfonso Mauricio (1611-12), Anna (1601-1666), Maria (b.1603), Maria Anna (1606-1646), and Margarita Francisca (1610-1617). Margarita died in 1611 at the age of 27 years. Velasquez painted the painting on which Goya based his etching sometime after the death of Margarita.
4. During his kingship, Philip III saw the landed aristocracy in power and the rule of the *validos,* or royal favorites. The first of these "favorites", lasting to 1618, was the Duke of Lerma and afterwards Lerma's son, the Duke of Uceda. In foreign affairs, the monarchy followed a peaceful policy ending the war with England through the Treaty of London of 1604 and maintaining the hegemony in Europe by relying on the influence of dynastic relations with other reigning families, particularly those in Austria and France.

D MARGARITA DE AUSTRIA REYNA DE ESPAÑA, MUGER DE PHELIPE III.
Pintura de D. Diego Velazquez, del tamaño del natural, en el Real Palacio de MADRID, dibujada y grabada, por D. Fran.co Goya Pintor, año de 1778.

69. FRANCISCO JOSE de GOYA y LUCIENTES
Fuendetodos 1746 - 1828 Bordeaux

Tal para qual (1st edition), 1799
Two of a Kind

Etching, aquatint and drypoint on laid paper
200 x 150 mm.; 7 7/8 x 5 7/8 inches

Reference:
Caprichos, plate 5
Delteil 42
Harris 40.III.1

Notes:
1. A very fine impression on laid paper from the 1st edition of 1799.
2. The Prado text explanation for this work is as follows:

> *Muchas veces se ha disputado si los hombres son peores que las mujeres o lo contrario.*
> *Los vicios de unos y otros vienen de la mala education donde quiera que los hombres*
> *sean perversos las mujeres lo seran tambien. Tan buena cabeza tiene la señorita que*
> *se representa en esta estampa como el pisaverde que le está dando conversacion, y en*
> *cuanto á las dos viejas tan infame as la una como la otra.*
> (Many times it has been disputed whether men are worse than women or the opposite. In
> any case, the vices, in both cases, come from a bad upbringing in which men are supposed to
> be perverse and women also. The woman represented in this work has as knowing a head as
> that of the young man who is seen conversing. Insofar as the two old women are concerned,
> each one is as evil-appearing as the other).

3. The other texts on this work invariably give it a "political" explanation. The Juan March Foundation's
    text, for example, refers to Queen Maria-Luisa and her lover Manuel Godoy and calls the meeting
    depicted as clearly that of two adulterers and notes that the two women in the background, pretending to
    pray, underline "the vicious aspect of this rendez-vous". The Ayala manuscript of about 1799-1803
    simply calls the subject of this etching: *Maria-Luisa y Godoy,* thus referring to Queen Maria-Luisa and
    her lover Manuel Godoy. At this time, Godoy was really governing Spain at the same time that King
    Carlos IV spent most of his time hunting and eating. In this respect, see Goya's painting *King Carlos IV
    in Hunting Costume,* 1799, in the Patrimonio Nacional, Palacio Real, Madrid.

Tal para qual.

70. FRANCISCO JOSE de GOYA y LUCIENTES
Fuendetodos 1746 - 1828 Bordeaux

Ni así la distingue (1st edition), 1799
He still cannot make her out

Etching, aquatint and drypoint on laid paper
200 x 150 mm.; 7 7/8 x 5 7/8 inches

Reference:
Caprichos, plate 7
Delteil 108
Harris 106.III.1

Notes:
1. A very fine impression on laid paper from the 1st edition of 1799.
2. This print plays on the difference between "to see" and "to perceive". Obviously, looking at the young lady's stance and her knowing smile, the young man, in spite of (or perhaps because of) his magnifying glass, does not appear to perceive her true nature. A broader interpretation of this work could consider it as an attack on a generally felt shortsightedness of the privileged classes of the time. The Biblioteca Nacional text is much more to the point:

> *Se ciegan tanto los hombres luxuriosos, que ni con tente distinguen que la señora que obsequian, es une ramera.*
> (Lecherous men close their eyes so much that not even with a magnifying glass can they distinguish that the lady whom they are pursuing is a prostitute).

3. The Prado text explanation is more general:

> *Como a de distinguirla? Para conocer lo que ella es no basta el anteojos necisita juicio y practica del mundo el esto es precisamente lo que falta al pobre caballero.*
> (How can he make her out? In order to know what she is, a monocle would not be enough. There would be needed both worldly judgement and practical experience. This is precisely what this poor gentleman lacks).

7

Ni asi la distingue.

71. FRANCISCO JOSE de GOYA y LUCIENTES
Fuendetodos 1746 - 1828 Bordeaux

¡Que se la llevaron! (1st edition), 1799
They Carried her Away!

Etching and aquatint
215 x 150 mm.; 8 1/2 x 5 7/8 inches

References:
Caprichos, plate 8; Delteil 45; Harris 43 III.1

Notes:
1. A very fine impression on laid paper from the 1st edition of 1799.
2. The violence of this scene, differing from most of the other *Caprichos,* anticipates the scenes of murder and rape to appear later in Goya's *Desastres de la Guerra.* In this work, one of the abductors is wearing the robe of a monk. This could be interpreted as an attack on the sometimes violent and illicit activities of the religious orders in Spain. The sentiment of passions unleashed in this scene is highlighted by the violent contrasts of the blacks and whites. Adding to the enigma of this work is the "mutual embrace of abductor and abducted" which might indicate some sort of "perverse dependence of the victim upon her assailant". (See: Tomlinson *Graphic Evolutions : The Print Series of Francisco Goya,* pp. 19-20).

72. FRANCISCO JOSE de GOYA y LUCIENTES
Fuendetodos 1746 - 1828 Bordeaux

¡Linda Maestra! (1st edition), 1799
A Pretty Teacher!

Etching and aquatint
210 x 150 mm.; 8 5/16 x 5 7/8 inches

References:
Caprichos, plate 68; Delteil 105; Harris 103 III.1

Notes:
1. A very fine impression on laid paper from the 1st edition of 1799.
2. The exact nature of this subject is indicated by the owl (*buho*) which dominates this whole scene from the upper right. The *buho* in Spanish is the symbol of the street-walker or prostitute. This is made explicit in the Madrid Biblioteca Nacional text: "The old witches give them (young girls) lessons to enable them to fly (*volar* = "practice the art of prostitution") throughout the world, setting them off for the first time even if it be with only a broomstick between their legs (*Las viejas ...las dan lecciones de volar por el; mundo, metiendolas por primera vez, aunque sea un palo de escoba entre las piernas*).

8

Que se la llevaron!

Linda maestra!

58. After Nicolas Lancret (1690-1743)   etching

We dedicate this publication to Kristof, Kristine, Gregoire, Geraldine and Christopher
umj and rsj